The Chemistry

of the OH Group

The Chemistry

of the OH Group

Leallyn B. Clapp

Department of Chemistry
Brown University

PRENTICE-HALL, INC., Englewood Cliffs, N.J.

FOUNDATIONS OF MODERN CHEMISTRY SERIES

Robert W. Parry and Henry Taube, Editors

Preface

Organic chemistry is commonly given one or two chapters in general chemistry textbooks and one (or none) in high school textbooks in which

a. to extol the virtues of better living through chemistry (Nylon, tranquilizers, isooctane, Styrofoam, and Corfam);

b. to imbibe the new alphabet soup (LSD, DDT, DNA, DMSO, EDTA);

c. to show the helical structure of a protein;

d. to please the aspiring scholar with the Geneva system of nomenclature which he can display to his less informed peers; and

e. to print a picture of the plumbing of an oil refinery in a New Jersey swamp.

I maintain that this treatment merely tends to spread about a thin layer of ignorance, a dangerous thing.

The time spent in this way might better be used to learn the chemistry of one functional group, especially as the organic chemists appear to be abandoning the time-honored method of introducing organic chemistry as functional group chemistry. The functional group is not to be attached only to carbon but to aluminum, boron, nitrogen, sulfur, phosphorus, or any other element in the Periodic Table. In this way, hopefully, the split between organic and inorganic chemistry need never occur.

Concentration on the chemistry of one group allows a deeper penetration of the relationship of properties and structure. What better group to pick than the OH group, for if the student has studied chemistry at all he will already know some of the chemistry of water. The modification in properties exhibited when the atom attached to OH is changed from H in water to S in sulfuric acid or to a metal in a hydroxide or to some other element is the subject of this book.

The gross character of the OH group is tied to unsophisticated notions of electronegativity. Gross acidity in the oxygen-containing acids of formula $(HO)_nMO_m$ may be predicted by Pauling's rules. An extension of Pauling's idea is made to other substitutions on the central atom M.

The beginning student deserves to know why we cannot by looking at structure alone predict acid strength more accurately than we can. More elaborate theories will, of course, do better in such predictions than Pauling's simple rules where the limit is about ± 2 powers of 10. The argument is based on R. P. Bell's excellent presentation of the problems involved in predicting acid strength in solutions. Freshmen deserve to know some of the unanswered chemical problems of the day. The elementary descriptive notions of thermodynamics given in this treatment are with us in beginning college courses now and are even trickling down into high school chemistry.

The greatest changes in the environment of an OH group can be made when the central atom holding the OH group is carbon. A search is made in Chapter 2 for likenesses and differences in the chemistry of water and alcohols.

One can put a lot of chemistry under one roof with a look at the reactions of covalent halides and oxyhalides with water (displacement of halogen by OH). This allows for a generalized treatment of the hydrolysis of halogens on a variety of central atoms. The budding chemist can thus learn the descriptive chemistry of a functional group on many different central atoms, a joy not sufficiently appreciated by the inorganic chemist.

After learning some of the chemistry of the OH group, the reader is asked to try to transfer his knowledge to another system—from the oxygen system of water to the nitrogen system of ammonia. This concept of isosteres as a guide to learning new chemistry was first suggested by Irving Langmuir and explored in the nitrogen system by E. C. Franklin.

When the high school student comes to college thinking that sulfuric acid is a flat molecule in which hydrogen is attached to sulfur, we have no one to blame but ourselves. We hide information from students by the way we write formulas, e.g., H_2SO_4 instead of $(HO)_2SO_2$. If we could write a tetrahedral formula for sulfuric acid on the blackboard with 3-D chalk the three-dimensional nature of structures might be easier to sell from the beginning. In this book there is an attempt to show the third dimension in chemistry, often by equations with a perspective.

Compounds containing OH groups suffer from intermolecular and intramolecular atrophy, two interesting conditions that are by strict dictionary usage limited to living things. The loss of water from the OH function in this inanimate case leads to *ortho*, *meta*, and *para* acids by intramolecular atrophy and to polyacids and new functions (ethers, esters, and anhydrides) by intermolecular atrophy. Why do we represent nitric acid with a single formula but write several phosphoric acids? This problem is examined in Chapter 4.

A few internal exercises (within chapters) are intended to be solved at the time the reader comes to them to fix in his mind what he has just read. Exercises at the ends of chapters apply more generally to the content of the whole chapter or tie together concepts from previous chapters.

The author acknowledges the fundamental suggestions made by Professor Henry Taube, an editor of this series, who read the manuscript, and important ideas received from Professors Robert M. Sherman and John O. Edwards at various stages in its development. The principal ideas were aired before a panel of the Advisory Council on College Chemistry in 1964 at Tulane University and before high school teachers in a number of Summer Institutes. The author acknowledges certain refinements resulting from suggestions made by teachers in these discussions.

Leallyn B. Clapp

Contents

ix

The Chemistry

of the OH Group

1

The
Hydroxy
Group

The Functional Group

One of the great simplifying principles in all of chemistry is the idea that a group of atoms will cling together through a chemical reaction or a series of chemical reactions. For classification, when the group carries a charge, the name *ion* is used for the charged species and the name *radical* for a *group* that maintains its integrity throughout a chemical reaction. The reader is already acquainted with such radicals as CN, OH, SO_4, SCN, CO_3, and PO_4 that take the following charges as ions:

$$CN^-, OH^-, SO_4^=, SCN^-, CO_3^=, \text{ and } PO_4^{3-}$$

When attached to an atom by a covalent bond, the group often dominates the properties of the entire molecule as reflected in wet[1] chemical reactions. In such a case the group may be thought of as functional, since it determines for the most part the properties (or function) of the molecule. Whereas the concept of a functional group is conventional in organic chemistry, the term "radical" or "ion" is more common in inorganic chemistry.

If we designate the remainder of the

---

[1] For the most part the discussion in this book is limited to solution chemistry (wet reactions) in contrast to reactions in the gas phase. Radicals often lose their integrity in gas phase reactions.

1

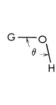

FIGURE 1.1 (a) The functional group —OH attached to the group G in which the bond angle θ at the oxygen is about 100–105°. The bond angle of 100–105° is determined by the interplay of electrostatic repulsions among bonded and nonbonded electron pairs on oxygen. For a discussion of this phenomenon, see R. J. Gillespie, J. Chem. Ed., **40**, 295 (1963). (b) A molecule where the group G consists of a tetrahedral central atom M with the functional group OH and three other groups a, b, and c attached at angles φ of about 109°. The angle φ will deviate only a little from 109°28'; the size of the angle is dictated by the geometry of a tetrahedron.

molecule as G (group) and take OH as one such functional group, the general formula G—OH can be applied to a series of substances. In reality there are at least three variables in G—OH which we must examine to describe the chemistry of compounds fitting the general formula.

The group G (Fig. 1.1a) may in fact consist of a central atom, M, which itself has other atoms or fragments attached to it. In Fig. 1.1b, three such fragments (a, b, and c) are shown attached to the central atom M. Besides the influence of M on the properties of the OH as a functional group, it may be that a, b, and c will also exert influences on the properties of OH. The influence of a, b, and c may be exerted through chemical bonds or across space, but in either case the influence will be of an electrostatic character. To get a picture of the chemistry of a functional group, then, we must examine (1) the atom M immediately attached, (2) the atoms or groups a, b, and c attached to this central atom, and (3) the function itself.

Character of the Central Atom, M

Since we cannot simultaneously examine all three variables (just mentioned) we will first look at the direct connection (chemical bond) between G and OH. We can set aside for the moment the problem of the angle between bonds (θ in Fig. 1.1), since the bond angle will not vary much with a change in G for the same functional group (OH). What influence does the atom M immediately attached have on the OH function?

A general property of atoms that you have already encountered—*electronegativity*[2]—is a periodic property. The electronegativity of an atom is a measure of the tendency of that atom in a molecule to attract electrons to itself (Table 1.1). Each element to the right of another in the same row of the periodic table has a higher electronegativity. In the second row, for

[2] Electronegativity is a secondary composite property of an element empirically determined from primary physicochemical properties such as ionization potentials and electron affinities. Other primary properties such as the radius of an atom and its charge density could be used in various cases to correlate the properties of elements. Electronegativity is simply a handy empiricism to select for the purpose at hand because it does correlate a number of properties.

Table 1.1 ELECTRONEGATIVITY OF CENTRAL ATOMS

I	II	III	IV	V	VI	VII
Li—OH	Be—OH	B—OH	C—OH	N—OH	O—OH	F—OH
1.0	1.5	2.0	2.5	3.0	3.5	4.0
Na—OH	Mg—OH	Al—OH	Si—OH	P—OH	S—OH	Cl—OH
0.9	1.2	1.5	1.8	2.1	2.5	3.0

example, the electronegativities, according to the Pauling scale,[3] vary from 1.0 for lithium to 4.0 for fluorine. For these two extremes in the second row, the electronegativities of the three elements in MOH are shown above the formulas and the electronegativity differences between adjacent atoms in MOH are shown below. There is a large difference (2.5) between the electro-

Electronegativities, X	1.0 3.5 2.1	4.0 3.5 2.1
Formula	Li O H	F O H
Electronegativity differences, ΔX	2.5 1.4	0.5 1.4

negativities of lithium and oxygen, a small difference (0.5) between the electronegativity of fluorine and oxygen, and a constant difference (1.4), of course, between oxygen and hydrogen in the two examples. There are similar differences in the corresponding elements from the third row.

Electronegativities, X	0.9 3.5 2.1	3.0 3.5 2.1
Formula	Na O H	Cl O H
Electronegativity differences, ΔX	2.6 1.4	0.5 1.4

Can this information be used as a guide to the properties of real substances? Differences in electronegativity cannot be used as a guide to the *existence* of substances (FOH is unknown, for example), but let us examine some *known* substances.

The two substances lithium hydroxide (LiOH) and sodium hydroxide (NaOH) are described in general terms as bases. Sodium hydroxide (NaOH), like LiOH, is a strong base. In aqueous solution NaOH neutralizes acids, NaOH turns litmus blue, and NaOH reacts in other ways that we have learned to call "the behavior of a base." The formulas written as Li^+OH^- and Na^+OH^- more descriptively portray the character of the compounds in the solid state.

In aqueous solution the following reaction occurs (although the dissociation is incomplete)

$$LiOH_{(s)} + H_2O \longrightarrow Li^+_{(aq)} + OH^-_{(aq)}$$

but the following one does not

$$LiOH_{(s)} + H_2O \not\longrightarrow LiO^-_{(aq)} + H^+_{(aq)}$$

That is, the hydrogen and oxygen atoms in the ion (OH^-) cling together in reactions characteristic of lithium hydroxide and sodium hydroxide. The

---

[3] See reference at the end of this chapter.

3

bond between O and H in OH⁻ is strong, covalent in character, and does not break readily in ordinary wet chemical reactions. The OH group *behaves* as though it clings together in spite of the fact that there is a rapid exchange of hydrogen and deuterium in H_2O-D_2O mixtures in basic solution.

From these experiences in the laboratory we might be led to the rule that when there is a larger difference between the electronegativities of the alkali metal (Group I) and oxygen (the example at hand, Li—O, 2.5) than between oxygen and hydrogen (O—H, 1.4) the ions Li⁺ and OH⁻ will form rather than LiO⁻ and H⁺.

On the other hand, the electronegativity difference between the Group VII element (fluorine and chlorine) and oxygen is smaller (-0.5 and $+0.5$, respectively) than the electronegativity difference between oxygen and hydrogen (1.4). The first possible compound from this row in the periodic table (FOH) is unknown, but the second (ClOH) is known. Although both bonds (Cl—O and O—H) in ClOH are best described as covalent in character, the O—H bond is broken by action of bases in aqueous solution, and the compound ClOH is called *hypochlorous acid*. A solution of hypochlorous acid turns blue litmus red (excess H_3O^+).

In aqueous solution the following equation represents the predominant reaction

$$ClOH + H_2O \longrightarrow H_3O^+ + ClO^-_{(aq)}$$

and the following one does not

$$ClOH + H_2O \longrightarrow\!\!\!\!/\!\!\!\!\rightarrow Cl^+_{(aq)} + OH^-_{(aq)}$$

We do not overlook the observation that the electronegativity differences have a different algebraic sign in the two examples at hand.

F	O	Cl	O
4.0	3.5	3.0	3.5

Undoubtedly only the less electronegative of two atoms can occupy the central position in a complex ion or molecule. This may be the most important factor in determining the instability of FO^-, FO_2^-, FO_3^-, and FO_4^-, all of which are unknown in comparison with ClO^-, ClO_2^-, ClO_3^-, and ClO_4^-, all of which are known.

Can we then make a generalization for the MOH compounds from Groups I and VII? Indeed, it is justified. All the alkali metal hydroxides (LiOH, NaOH, KOH, RbOH, CsOH) and presumably FrOH are strong bases. All the Group VII hydroxy compounds (ClOH, BrOH, IOH) are acidic. Table 1.2 summarizes the electronegativity differences among the elements making up these compounds.

The electronegativity difference between the alkali metal and oxygen (ΔX_{M-O}) is greater than the constant electronegativity difference between oxygen and hydrogen ($\Delta X_{O-H} = 1.4$); all the compounds MOH of Group I elements are strong bases. We can say that in all reactions of MOH as a base, the bond breaks between M and O. Dissociation into M⁺ and OH⁻ is complete in all cases up to concentrations of at least one mole per liter of MOH.

Table 1.2 ELECTRONEGATIVITY DIFFERENCES BETWEEN BONDING ATOMS IN MOH FOR GROUPS I AND VII

Row in periodic table	Element M	Electronegativity X_M	Electroneg. diff. ΔX_{M-O}	Electroneg. oxygen	Electroneg. diff. ΔX_{O-H}
Group I					
2	Li	1.0	2.5	3.5	1.4
3	Na	0.9	2.6	3.5	1.4
4	K	0.8	2.7	3.5	1.4
5	Rb	0.8	2.7	3.5	1.4
6	Cs	0.7	2.8	3.5	1.4
Group VII					
2	F	4.0	−0.5	3.5	1.4
3	Cl	3.0	0.5	3.5	1.4
4	Br	2.8	0.7	3.5	1.4
5	I	2.5	1.0	3.5	1.4

In Group VII compounds of formula MOH the electronegativity difference between the halogen and oxygen (ΔX_{M-O}) is smaller than the constant electronegativity difference between oxygen and hydrogen ($\Delta X_{O-H} = 1.4$); the compounds MOH formed from Group VII are acids. We can say that when these compounds act as acids, the bond breaks between O and H. Furthermore, as ΔX_{M-O} increases, the acid strength of MOH decreases. This statement holds for M=Cl, Br, and I, but no data are available on AtOH, and FOH is unknown (see Table 3.1).

All numerical values of ΔX_{M-O} for elements of Group VII are smaller than ΔX_{M-O} for elements of Group I. Group VII compounds of formula MOH are weak acids; Group I compounds of formula MOH are strong bases.

The electronegativity of M, then, determines whether electron pairs are available on MO:⁻ or on :OH⁻.

$$\text{MOH} \longrightarrow \text{MO:}^- + \text{H}^+$$

$$\text{MOH} \longrightarrow \text{M}^+ + \text{:OH}^-$$

We must proceed cautiously if we are to apply these generalizations to other groups in the periodic table. In the first place, only elements in Groups I and VII will have a single atom or group attached to M; elements from other groups will have other atoms or auxiliary radicals attached to M, which may change the picture (page 41). However, Group II (alkaline earth) hydroxides are bases, and their base strengths increase as the electronegativity of M decreases (Table 1.3). That is, barium hydroxide, $Ba(OH)_2$, is a stronger base than magnesium hydroxide, $Mg(OH)_2$, which in turn is a stronger base than beryllium hydroxide, $Be(OH)_2$.

When the electronegativity differences ΔX_{M-O} and ΔX_{O-H} are more nearly equal, the generalization we have made is less useful and indeed sometimes misleading.

$$\overset{\Delta X_{M-O} \quad \Delta X_{O-H}}{\text{M——————O——————H}}$$

Table 1.3 ELECTRONEGATIVITY DIFFERENCES BETWEEN BONDING ATOMS IN MOH FOR GROUP II

Row	Element M	X_M	ΔX_{M-O}	ΔX_{O-H}
2	Be	1.5	2.0	1.4
3	Mg	1.2	2.3	1.4
4	Ca	1.0	2.5	1.4
5	Sr	1.0	2.5	1.4
6	Ba	0.9	2.6	1.4

It might be expected that as $\Delta X_{M-O} = \Delta X_{O-H}$, either bond in M—O—H might break, suggesting that in such cases MOH might act either as a base or as an acid (amphoterism). Examples can be found for which this is true (Al, Si, Sb).

X	1.5	3.5	2.1	1.8	3.5	2.1	1.9	3.5	2.1
	Al——	—O——	—H	Si——	—O——	—H	Sb——	—O——	—H
ΔX	2.0	1.4		1.7	1.4		1.6	1.4	

However, in two cases for which $\Delta X_1 = \Delta X_2$ the bonding is clearly acidic (P and Te) in known compounds and in the case of carbon the bonding must

X	2.1	3.5	2.1	2.1	3.5	2.1
	P——	—O——	—H	Te——	—O——	—H
ΔX	1.4	1.4		1.4	1.4	

of necessity be called neutral in spite of a small difference between ΔX_{M-O} and ΔX_{O-H}. The OH bond in C—OH is neutral in the same sense that the OH bond in water is neutral (compare Chapter 2).

X	2.5	3.5	2.1	2.1	3.5	2.1
	C——	—O——	—H	H——	—O——	—H
ΔX	1.0	1.4		1.4	1.4	

Electronegativity differences are therefore not a reliable criterion for predicting basic or acidic bond character unless the differences are marked. Caution must be exercised in using electronegativities for this purpose. It must mean that other factors enter into the determination of acid-base character, one obvious factor being what we can link together under the term *solvent effects*. The solvent may interact more strongly with one set of products than it does with the other (see, for example, the LiOH case, p. 3), thus favoring one mode of dissociation over the other.

Water

Two classes of compounds represented by formula MOH have been discussed in which M is a single atom, the Group I alkali hydroxides and the Group VII oxyhalogen acids, HOCl, HOBr, HOI. Water, HOH, is another known compound which fits the general formula. Every molecule is unique (by definition), but water is so peculiar in its behavior with respect to related molecules that it is often described as anomalous. The melting point and

6

boiling point of water are far higher than they should be (by comparison with other compounds) for the molecular mass of 18 (Tables 2.1 and 2.2). The greatest density of water is not at the freezing point as it is with other liquids, but near 4°C. Water also has a large specific heat and a large dielectric constant in comparison with other molecules consisting of fewer than five atoms. The bent structure of the water molecule (bond angle is

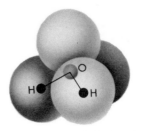

FIGURE 1.2 *Model showing the bent structure of the water molecule, bond angle 104°28'.*

104°28') helps to explain the anomalous properties of the solid form that are due to the crystal structure of ice and of the liquid form that are due to the less well defined structure of water.

However, the properties of water that are due to the OH group rather than the structure as a whole are similar in many ways to the properties of the OH group attached to atoms other than hydrogen, particularly carbon. It is the similarities of behavior of the functional group OH in water and in compounds with OH attached to carbon that we will stress at the moment.

Alcohols: A Homologous Series

When carbon is the central atom in MOH, it of course shares one pair of electrons with oxygen, but carbon must simultaneously share three pairs of electrons with other atoms.

$$:\overset{..}{\underset{..}{C}} : \overset{..}{\underset{..}{O}} : H$$

Carbon is tetravalent, an idea first suggested by Friedrich August Kekulé von Stradonitz in 1858 to account for the molecular formulas of many compounds known at the time and since found to have few exceptions among perhaps four million carbon compounds.

When the three pairs of electrons shown above on carbon (not shared in the picture) are shared with hydrogens, the resulting formula represents the first member of a series of compounds known as *alcohols*. The first member is methyl alcohol, CH_3OH (Fig. 1.3).

FIGURE 1.3 (a) *Electronic model of* CH_3OH. *Carbon and oxygen nuclei are shown as centers of two tetrahedral structures. Hydrogens embedded in electron pairs are shown as* +. (b) *Skeletal model of* CH_3OH *showing only relative positions of nuclei.*

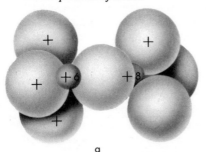

a

b

7

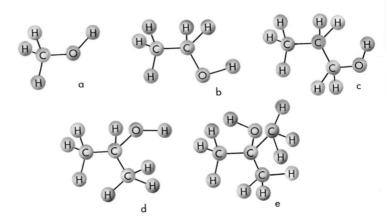

FIGURE 1.4   *Structures of (a) methyl alcohol; (b) ethyl alcohol; (c) n-propyl alcohol; (d) isopropyl alcohol; (e) tert-butyl alcohol.*

Carbon is unique in the periodic table in one very important property: it can form bonds with other carbons in long chains of tens, hundreds, even thousands of atoms. The longest chains known for other atom to atom linkages are silicon (25), nitrogen (4), and sulfur (8) in a cyclic elemental structure, and *n*, a large number, in some polysulfides and in plastic sulfur. Sulfur may be considered an exception to this unique property of carbon.

We can build the structural formulas of a family of alcohols from methyl alcohol as the starting point by making use of two well-established facts about carbon: (1) carbon always carries four bonds (Kekulé's idea of tetravalence to which there are very few exceptions); and (2) carbon will join carbon in stable linkages.

To show this in a formula, a hydrogen is replaced by a carbon carrying three H's. Replacement of H in the methyl alcohol formula (Fig. 1.4) by a CH_3 group gives the next member of the series, ethyl alcohol. Similar substitution for two hydrogens on carbon in methyl alcohol yields isopropyl alcohol and complete substitution of CH_3 groups for H's on carbon in methyl alcohol gives the compound called *tert*-butyl alcohol. (For *tert*, read "tertiary.")

Exercise 1.1.   By what manipulation in the formula for ethyl alcohol can the formula for *n*-propyl alcohol be obtained? (For *n*, read "normal.")

Manipulation of this kind on paper based on the two facts about carbon simply enables one to predict the possibility of existence of a family of compounds. All the alcohols shown above, and many more, have in fact been made in the laboratory. Such a family is called a *homologous series*. A homologous series may be defined as a family of compounds that (1) differ from each other by a CH_2 group or $(CH_2)_n$; (2) have similar chemical properties; and (3) have physical properties varying in a predictable manner.

In the alcohols considered, the molecular formulas CH_4O, C_2H_6O, C_3H_8O, and $C_4H_{10}O$, do differ by CH_2 groups as suggested in the first part of the definition. The other two consequences of the definition will be examined in the next chapter.

Nomenclature of Alcohols

A fundamental vocabulary of terms and names is needed before we can proceed with the discussion of properties of alcohols. Molecular formulas are of limited use in our study of carbon compounds because we shall be so interested in structure as a consequence of the directional nature of bonding in covalent compounds. A structural formula shows the three-dimensional arrangement of atoms within the molecule as well as the total molecular formula. The five structural formulas of the alcohols (Fig. 1.4) can be written expeditiously (and on a single line in a book) when three-dimensional character is not to be stressed (or to save time) with the more abbreviated representations:

$$CH_3- \text{ used for } H-\overset{\displaystyle H}{\underset{\displaystyle H}{|}}C-, \quad -CH_2- \text{ for } -\overset{\displaystyle H}{\underset{\displaystyle H}{|}}C-, \text{ and } -CHOH \text{ for } -\overset{\displaystyle H}{\underset{\displaystyle OH}{|}}C-$$

The five alcohols can then be written in *condensed* structural formulas as:

CH_3-OH	methyl alcohol
CH_3-CH_2-OH	ethyl alcohol
$CH_3-CH_2-CH_2-OH$	*n*-propyl alcohol
$CH_3-CHOH-CH_3$	isopropyl alcohol
$(CH_3)_3C-OH$	*tert*-butyl alcohol

The most important consequence of the directional nature of bonding in covalent compounds manifests itself in the existence of two different structural formulas for a three-carbon alcohol. Compounds with the same molecular formula but different structural formulas are called *isomers* and the phenomenon is called *isomerism*. Isopropyl and *n*-propyl alcohol (Fig. 1.4) are isomers.

To get at the problem of naming alcohols, we first need to name systematically the corresponding parent hydrocarbons (compounds of carbon and hydrogen only). The parent hydrocarbons (called *alkanes*) of the five alcohols have the OH groups replaced by hydrogens as shown in Table 1.4.

In Table 1.5, condensed structural formulas are given for two isomeric four-carbon hydrocarbons R—H, two isomeric three-carbon alcohols R—OH, four isomeric four-carbon alcohols R—OH, and all the corresponding isomeric alkyl groups R—.

Table 1.4 NOMENCLATURE OF ALKANES

Alcohol	*Parent hydrocarbon*	*Name*
CH_3-OH	CH_4	methane
CH_3-CH_2-OH	CH_3-CH_3	ethane
$CH_3-CH_2-CH_2-OH$	$CH_3-CH_2-CH_3$	propane
$CH_3-CHOH-CH_3$	$CH_3-CH_2-CH_3$	propane
$(CH_3)_3C-OH$	$CH_3-\overset{\displaystyle }{\underset{\displaystyle |}{C}}H-CH_3$	2-methylpropane
	CH_3	

Table 1.5 NOMENCLATURE OF VARIOUS COMPOUNDS AND GROUPS

Type	Type symbol	Number of carbons			
		1	2	3	4
Hydrocarbon (alkane)	RH	methane, CH_4	ethane, $CH_3—CH_3$	propane, $CH_3—CH_2—CH_3$	butane, $CH_3—CH_2—CH_2—CH_3$ 2-methylpropane, $CH_3—\overset{\displaystyle \,}{\underset{\displaystyle CH_3}{CH}}—CH_3$
Alcohol	R—OH	methanol $CH_3—OH$	ethanol $CH_3—CH_2OH$	1-propanol, $CH_3—CH_2—CH_2OH$ 2-propanol, $CH_3—CHOH—CH_3$	1-butanol, $CH_3—CH_2—CH_2—CH_2OH$ 2-butanol, $CH_3—CH_2—CHOH—CH_3$ 2-methyl-1-propanol, $CH_3—\overset{\displaystyle \,}{\underset{\displaystyle CH_3}{CH}}—CH_2OH$ 2-methyl-2-propanol, $(CH_3)_3COH$
Alkyl group	R—	methyl, $CH_3—$	ethyl, $CH_3—CH_2—$	*n*-propyl, $CH_3—CH_2—CH_2—$ isopropyl, $CH_3—\underset{\displaystyle |}{CH}—CH_3$	*n*-butyl, $CH_3—CH_2—CH_2—CH_2—$ *sec*-butyl, $CH_3—CH_2—\underset{\displaystyle |}{CH}—CH_3$ isobutyl, $(CH_3)_2CH—CH_2—$ *tert*-butyl, $(CH_3)_3C—$

The first accepted attempt to give systematic names to carbon compounds came from an International Congress meeting at Geneva, Switzerland, in 1892. Two subsequent revisions and extensions to new compounds from the International Union of Chemistry at Liege (1930) and the International Union of Pure and Applied Chemistry at Amsterdam (1949) have been made in what is called the *Geneva System* of nomenclature. The Geneva System is universally accepted so that chemists not able to read a particular language can still read names and decipher formulas in that language. Trivial names are still often used locally.

The rules for naming alcohols depend on earlier rules for the parent hydrocarbons.

1. Each homologous series has its own ending: for alkanes, *ane*; for an alcohol, *ol*.

2. Stems are formed from the common names of members of the alkane series (Table 1.4) by dropping the ending *ane* (for example: *meth*ane, *eth*ane, *prop*ane, *but*ane); for higher members of the homologous series, Greek stems follow (five carbons, *pent*ane; six carbons, *hex*ane; etc.). For an alcohol, the final *e* in the name for an alkane is dropped and *ol* added. For example,

$$CH_3—CH_3 \qquad\qquad CH_3—CH_2—OH$$

ethane   ethanol

10

3. Names for alkyl groups necessary in branched-chain compounds use *yl* endings on stems from common names. For example, methane has the stem *meth* to which *yl* is added to give the alkyl group, methyl. For other groups that will be used frequently, see Table 1.5.

4. Branched-chain alkanes are named as derivatives of the longest straight chain in the molecule as parent compound. If there are two chains of equal length, the chain with the most branches is chosen as parent and the chain is given its stem name. The chain is numbered in the direction to give the branches the smallest numbers. In alcohols, the longest chain containing the hydroxy group determines the stem.

$$\overset{5}{C}H_3-\overset{4}{C}H_2-\overset{3}{C}H_2-\overset{|2\ \ \overset{1}{C}H_3}{\underset{|}{C}}-\overset{1}{C}H_3$$
$$\underset{CH_3}{\overset{CH_3}{\ }}$$

is numbered from right to left, not left to right.

$$\overset{1}{C}H_3-\overset{2}{C}H-\overset{3}{C}H-\overset{4}{C}H_2-\overset{5}{C}H_3$$
$$\underset{CH_3\ \ CH_3}{|\ \ \ \ |}$$

is numbered from left to right.

5. The names of the branches are attached as prefixes to the parent name with the number giving the position of the branch on the chain. The number precedes the name of the alkyl group and is followed by a hyphen. A number is repeated if two branches appear at the same position. Numbers are separated by commas.

The examples in Rule 4 above are named 2,2-dimethylpentane and 2,3-dimethylpentane, respectively.

6. In alcohols, the hydroxy group is given the smaller number if alkyl groups also appear as branches. (See below, 3-methyl-2-butanol, *not* 2-methyl-3-butanol.)

The following examples and those in Table 1.5 are illustrative of the rules.

$$\overset{4}{C}H_3-\overset{3}{C}H-\overset{2}{C}H-\overset{1}{C}H_3$$
$$\underset{CH_3\ \ OH}{|\ \ \ \ |}$$

3-methyl-2-butanol

$$\overset{5}{C}H_3-\overset{4}{C}H-\overset{3}{C}H_2-\overset{3|}{C}-\overset{2}{C}H-\overset{1}{C}H_3$$
$$\underset{{}^6CH_3\ \ \ \ \ \ \ HO\ \ CH_3}{}$$

with CH_2-CH_3 on carbon 3

2,5-dimethyl-3-ethyl-3-hexanol

Common names are often used for alcohols of four carbons or less. Common names of these alcohols may be obtained by adding the word "alcohol" to the appropriate common name for the alkyl group (Table 1.5).

Exercise 1.2. Write structural formulas for the five isomers having the formula C_6H_{14} and name them by the Geneva System.

Exercise 1.3. Write structural formulas for the nine alcohols of formula $C_5H_{11}OH$ and name them by the Geneva System.

Exercise 1.4. How many alcohols of formula $C_6H_{13}OH$ can you draw structures for? (*Answer:* 13)

Exercise 1.5. Write the structural formulas for
   a. 2,2,4-trimethylpentane
   b. 2,5-dimethyl-3-ethyl-4-octanol

Suggested References

Pauling, L., *The Nature of the Chemical Bond*, Cornell University Press, Ithaca, N.Y. (1960), 3rd ed.
Sanderson, R. T., *Chemical Periodicity*, Reinhold Publ. Corp., New York (1960).

2

Water

and Alcohols

It is obvious from the title of this chapter that water and alcohols must have enough properties in common to warrant their study together. The representations of the formula for water and of the general formula for an alcohol (below) indicate that their bond angles at the oxygen atom are nearly the same—about 105°. What other properties in common do water and alcohols have?

$$H : \overset{\cdot\cdot}{\underset{\cdot\cdot}{O}} \qquad\qquad R : \overset{\cdot\cdot}{\underset{\cdot\cdot}{O}}$$
$$H \qquad\qquadH$$

Water   Alcohols

Studying water and alcohols together allows us to pose certain other questions. For instance: At the laboratory bench, how is the simple change of an alkyl (R) group for an H atom reflected in the bulk properties of the molecules? and: Can we correlate melting points, boiling points, solubilities, and densities with any simple property of the molecules involved such as mass, shape, surface area, volume, or electron density around nuclei? We must admit right away that chemists are still looking for such correlations; that none is satisfactory for more than a limited number of closely related substances. The degree of satisfaction of such correlations depends on the inquirer's acceptance of

13

any statement defining "closely related substances." We will examine the correlations of boiling points, solubilities, and densities in a series of alcohols and water.

The Boiling Point of Water

The boiling point of water is 100°C; of methyl alcohol, 65°C; and of ethyl alcohol, 78°C. All three are higher than "expected" for the molecular masses of 18, 32, and 46, respectively. They also are not in ascending order with respect to molecular mass.

What are the "expectations" for boiling points of compounds? By what standard are we privileged to call these three boiling points unexpectedly high? The answer is "by comparison with boiling points of 'well-behaved' compounds." As a first property to examine, by "well-behaved" compounds we will mean as large a group of compounds as we can find whose boiling points correlate with molecular mass. Other compounds, then, by this standard are said to be "anomalous"—to behave in an unexpected manner.

The choice of molecular mass as the variable with which to compare boiling points is arbitrary. Other properties have been used in order to get better correlations with boiling points, including density and surface area, but without more marked success than molecular mass.

As another standard of comparison, let us use molecules containing the same number of electrons (isoelectronic molecules) as in water molecules (10), and nearly the same masses. The boiling point of water in this comparison (Table 2.1) is also very high: 81° above the next highest (HF), and 346° above that of neon (Fig. 2.1). We therefore call the boiling point of water anomalous or unexpected with respect to those of the other isoelectronic substances.

In another series, the hydrides of Group VI (Table 2.2), the anomalous character of water also stands out. Water boils 100° higher than the fourth member of this series, H_2Te, whose molecular mass is more than seven times that of water. Except for water, however, this series follows the rule that increasing boiling points follow increasing molecular mass or increasing total number of electrons (Fig. 2.1).

An explanation of the anomalous boiling point of water in comparison with alcohols, isoelectronic molecules, and Group VI hydrides brings us to the phenomenon of hydrogen bonding, fundamental to an understanding of the properties of "associated" liquids (also solids or gases). When a highly electronegative atom, F or O for example, is bound to hydrogen in a compound, there is a net electrostatic attraction between the electronic coating of the fluorine (or oxygen) of one molecule and the highly concentrated

Table 2.1 BOILING POINTS OF FIVE ISOELECTRIC SUBSTANCES

	CH_4	NH_3	H_2O	HF	Ne
Number of electrons	10	10	10	10	10
Molecular mass	16	17	18	20	20
bp (°C)	−161	−33	100	19	−246
fp (°C)	−184	−77	0	−92	−249

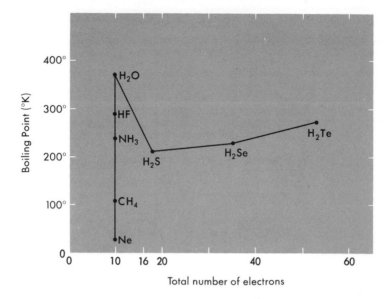

Total number of electrons

FIGURE 2.1 *Boiling points of a series of isoelectronic molecules* CH_4, NH_3, H_2O, HF, *and* Ne *and a series of Group VI hydrides,* H_2O, H_2S, H_2Se, *and* H_2Te.

positive nuclear charge of the proton in the next molecule. The proton bonded in one molecule, thus attracted to the electronegative atom in a second molecule (Fig. 2.2), may result in a polymeric cluster.

This is a special case of the more general phenomenon of net attraction between neutral molecules that have dipole moments. Qualitatively this statement will appear reasonable by examination of Fig. 6.2, a vector representation of the permanent dipole in the water molecule. Sanderson[1] has estimated that the dipole moment of water (1.84 Debye units) can be accounted for if the partial charge on each hydrogen is $+0.12$. This puts a partial negative charge on the oxygen of -0.24 of an electron. Consequently, in the area above the oxygen of the water molecule (Fig. 6.2) there will be an attraction for the proton of another water molecule. The attraction of the strongly electronegative (F or O) atom for the proton of another molecule is called a *hydrogen bond* or *hydrogen bridge* since it bonds, bridges, or acts as a buffer between the two electronegative atoms. Consequently, water and hydrogen fluoride (Fig. 2.2) are said to be *associated liquids*. If their formulas are more correctly represented as $(HF)_m$ and $(H_2O)_n$, their boiling points may be considered more rational in terms of realistic "molecular" masses.

Table 2.2 BOILING POINTS OF GROUP VI HYDRIDES, H_2M

Formula, H_2M	Molecular mass	bp, °C
H_2O	18	100
H_2S	34	-60
H_2Se	81	-42
H_2Te	129.5	0

[1] R. T. Sanderson, *Chemical Periodicity*, Reinhold Publ. Corp., New York (1960), p. 168.

15

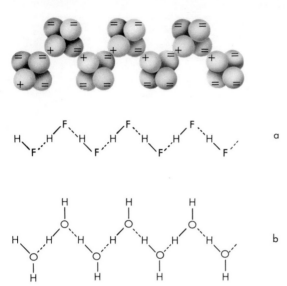

FIGURE 2.2 *Hydrogen bonding in (a) hydrogen fluoride, (b) water, and (c) ammonia. The charge cloud model at the top of the figure will serve for water and ammonia if two (or three) + charges (protons) are inserted in each four-cloud cluster for water (for ammonia). [Redrawn from Chemical Systems, McGraw-Hill Book Co., New York (1964), p. 730.]*

In the isoelectric series of Table 2.1 the associated liquids, HF and H_2O, have high boiling points in comparison with methane (CH_4) and neon, which cannot form hydrogen bonds. Ammonia (NH_3), the fifth compound, of intermediate boiling point, has a central atom (N) of moderate electronegativity, and forms weak hydrogen bonds (Fig. 2.2).

$$C \qquad N \qquad O \qquad F$$
$$2{\cdot}5 \qquad 3{\cdot}0 \qquad 3{\cdot}5 \qquad 4{\cdot}0$$

It may be noted that water, with two hydrogens on oxygen, has the possibility of forming a three-dimensional network of hydrogen bonds (Fig. 2.3),

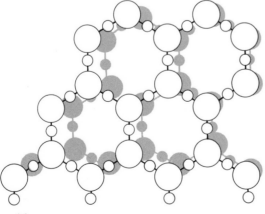

FIGURE 2.3 *Structure of ice, showing three-dimensional network of hydrogen bonds.*

16

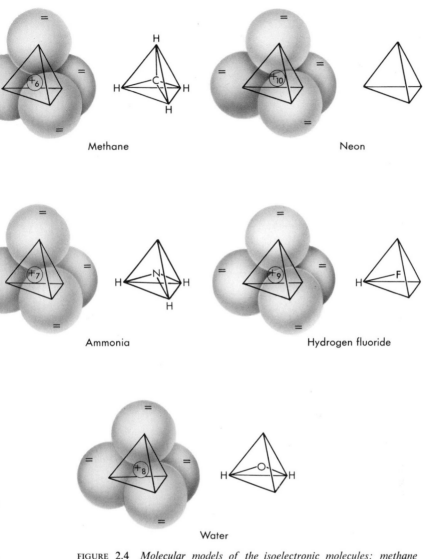

Methane

Neon

Ammonia

Hydrogen fluoride

Water

FIGURE 2.4 *Molecular models of the isoelectronic molecules: methane* (CH$_4$), *ammonia* (NH$_3$), *water* (H$_2$O), *hydrogen fluoride* (HF), *and neon* (Ne).

whereas HF and NH$_3$ can form only a linear (or zigzag) chain or rings (Fig. 2.2). Water does, indeed, have a much higher boiling point than either of its neighbors in the isoelectronic series that we are considering. The three-dimensional ice lattice which is known from X-ray crystallography to portray the structure of ice, is not entirely destroyed when the ice melts. In a qualitative way this would account for the high boiling point of water and suggests again the molecular formula (H$_2$O)$_n$, where n is an unknown but probably a small number.

Exercise 2.1. Why is it that CH$_4$ cannot form hydrogen bonds? Devise an answer by referring to Fig. 2.2 and Fig. 2.4.

17

Boiling Points of Alcohols

Not unreasonably, alcohols, which have OH groups, form hydrogen bonds just as water does.

$$\overset{\text{R}}{:\overset{..}{\text{O}}:\text{H}}\overset{\text{R}}{:\overset{..}{\text{O}}:\text{H}}\overset{\text{R}}{:\overset{..}{\text{O}}:\text{H}}$$

However, because of the R groups the network is limited to chains, as in the case of ammonia and hydrogen fluoride, rather than to a three-dimensional network, as in water. Alcohols have lower boiling points than water *until* a four-carbon alcohol is reached, with a molecular mass four times that of water (Table 2.3). Alcohols are associated in hydrogen bonding to some extent, however. Presumptive evidence for this is available by comparison of the boiling points of alcohols with the boiling points of hydrocarbons (Table 2.3) of similar molecular mass. The hydrocarbons boil much lower than the alcohol of corresponding molecular mass. For example, the boiling point of *n*-propyl alcohol, molecular mass 60, is 98°, while that of butane, molecular mass 58, is 0°.

The two isomers of molecular mass 46 in Table 2.3 boil 102° apart. The alcohol, the higher boiling compound, is capable of forming hydrogen bonds while the ether, CH_3—O—CH_3, has no hydrogen on an electronegative atom (oxygen) and hence is incapable of hydrogen bonding with itself.[2] The final compound in the table, carbon tetrachloride, which cannot form hydrogen bonds, has a boiling point (76°) near that of ethyl alcohol (78°), but the molecular mass of CCl_4 is more than three times that of ethyl alcohol.

Examination of the boiling points of the alcohols themselves in Table 2.4 reveals that increased molecular mass is reflected by increased boiling point in a regular manner, provided that alcohols of similar structure are selected. When the functional group is on the end of a chain (1-ols in the table), the boiling point increment is actually a constant of 20° for the interval C_2 to C_6 in the series as each CH_2 group is added.

Number of carbons in the alcohol	C_1	C_2	C_3	C_4	C_5	C_6	C_7	C_8
bp, °C	66	78	98	118	138	158	176	195

Table 2.3 BOILING POINTS OF H_2O, R—OH, AND OTHER COMPOUNDS

	Associated liquids			Nonassociated liquids	
Formula	Molecular mass	Boiling point, °C	Formula	Molecular mass	Boiling point, °C
H—OH	18	100	CH_4	16	−161
CH_3—OH	32	66	CH_3—CH_3	30	−89
C_2H_5—OH	46	78	CH_3—O—CH_3	46	−24
n-C_3H_7—OH	60	98	$CH_3(CH_2)_2CH_3$	58	0
n-C_4H_9—OH	74	118	CCl_4	152	76

[2] The electronegative oxygen atom in the ether might, however, attract the H in a molecule such as HCl to form a hydrogen bond.

Table 2.4 PHYSICAL PROPERTIES OF ALCOHOLS

Formula	Geneva name	mp (°C)	bp (°C)	Density (g/ml)	Solubility in H_2O
CH_3OH	methanol	−98	66	0.792	miscible
C_2H_5OH	ethanol	−115	78	0.789	miscible
C_3H_7OH	1-propanol	−127	98	0.804	miscible
C_4H_9OH	1-butanol	−90	118	0.810	9.0%
$C_5H_{11}OH$	1-pentanol	−79	138	0.818	2.7%
$C_6H_{13}OH$	1-hexanol	−52	158	0.822	0.6%
$C_7H_{15}OH$	1-heptanol	35	176	0.824	0.2%
$C_8H_{17}OH$	1-octanol	−17	195	0.829	0.05%
$C_{12}H_{25}OH$	1-dodecanol	24	256	0.831	insoluble (not measurable)
$C_{18}H_{37}OH$	1-octadecanol	58			insoluble (not measurable)
C_3H_7OH	2-propanol	−90	83	0.785	miscible
C_4H_9OH	2-methyl-1-propanol	−108	108	0.802	10.0%
$C_5H_{11}OH$	3-methyl-1-butanol	—	130	0.810	3.3%
$C_6H_{13}OH$	4-methyl-1-pentanol	—	148	0.824	0.6%
$C_7H_{15}OH$	5-methyl-1-hexanol	—	169	0.831	0.2%

The increment in boiling point gradually decreases (at C_7 and C_8) as might be expected since the increment in molecular mass ($CH_2 = 14$) gradually becomes a smaller percentage of the total molecular mass.

Branched-chain alcohols (lower part of Table 2.4) have lower boiling points than the corresponding isomeric straight chain (upper part of Table 2.4) alcohols. However, the series of five branched-chain homologs has boiling points gradually increasing with each CH_2 group added, in the same way as the straight-chain alcohols.

The trends apparent in the straight-chain and branched-chain alcohols are also exhibited in other closely related series.

Melting points of substances follow no recognizable pattern with respect to chain length or molecular mass as can be seen in this series (Table 2.4). Melting points depend on subtle differences in structure of the solid and liquid phases. The packing pattern in the three-dimensional crystal depends mostly on size and shape, and the melting point depends in part on how much change toward randomness occurs when the liquid phase obtains.

Solubility of Alcohols in Water

"Like dissolves like" is an adage that has been used in chemistry for a long time as a working rule for guessing solubilities of substances. To use the rule we must examine the connotations of "like." You are acquainted with the further household statement, "oil and water do not mix." If the principal constituents of petroleum are taken as the "oil," we may identify "oil" chemically as a hydrocarbon (compound of carbon and hydrogen) of which one set of examples is the homologous series, alkanes, beginning with CH_4 (Tables 1.4 and 1.5).

We may get a hint concerning one difference between oil and water by looking at the electronegativities of the atoms in the three formulas: CH_4, CH_3OH, and H_2O. In Chapter 1, we said that the large difference in electronegativity between the alkali metals and oxygen could be correlated with

19

ease of bond cleavage between the two atoms, and we wrote the formula for sodium hydroxide showing a complete separation of charge to form two ions. Experimental evidence covering the character of sodium hydroxide justifies this designation.

$$\text{Na}^+ \quad :\overset{\cdot\cdot}{\underset{\cdot\cdot}{O}}: \quad H^-$$

Between atoms of the same element, such as chlorine, wherein the electronegativity difference is of necessity zero,

$$:\overset{\cdot\cdot}{\underset{\cdot\cdot}{Cl}}:\overset{\cdot\cdot}{\underset{\cdot\cdot}{Cl}}:$$

the bond is described as pure covalent, and charge separation in the molecule would not be expected. Where atoms of different elements are involved in bond formation, we might expect in-between stages of charge separation—that is, a range between ionic and pure covalent bonds. The intermediate type is called a *polar covalent bond.*

In the cases at hand, the electronegativities of carbon, hydrogen, and oxygen on the Pauling scale are 2.5, 2.1, and 3.5, respectively. In methane,

$$\underset{C}{\overset{2.5}{}}\text{———}\underset{O}{\overset{3.5}{}} \qquad \underset{H}{\overset{2.1}{}}\text{———}\underset{O}{\overset{3.5}{}}$$

$$\underset{H}{\overset{\diagdown 2.1}{}} \qquad\qquad \underset{H}{\overset{\diagdown 2.1}{}}$$

wherein the difference in electronegativity of carbon and hydrogen is only 0.4, the bonds are only slightly polar in character. Furthermore, the four C—H bonds are symmetrically arranged about the carbon (Fig. 2.4), and the molecule as a whole can be described as strictly nonpolar in character.

$$\underset{H}{\overset{\displaystyle H}{|}}\;\;H\text{—}\underset{|}{C}\text{—}H\;\;\underset{|}{|}\;\;\underset{H}{\overset{\displaystyle H}{|}}\;\;H\text{—}\underset{|}{C}\text{—}O\;\;\overset{\diagdown}{}\;\;H\text{—}O\overset{\diagdown}{}$$

On the other hand, the bond polarity in C—O—H (methyl alcohol, Fig. 2.5) will be close to that in H—O—H (Fig. 2.4), since the electronegativity differences are comparable in magnitude. The total moments in the two molecules also are not markedly different, since the bond angles are comparable (page 20 and Table 6.1).

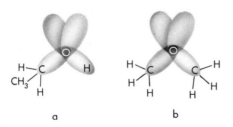

FIGURE 2.5 *Unshared pairs of electrons on oxygen in (a) ethyl alcohol and (b) dimethyl ether.*

Water and methyl alcohol molecules are, indeed, called *polar molecules*. One of the macroscopic properties (observable at the bench) that reflects polar character is the tendency to dissolve other substances. It is this tendency to dissolve substances that is described in the aforementioned adage, "like dissolves like." Translated into chemical terms, polar solvents tend to dissolve polar solutes, and nonpolar solvents tend to dissolve nonpolar solutes. (The chemical statement using the phrase "tend to" is more conservative than the statement "like dissolves like," and hence safer.)

Water and methyl alcohol are similar to each other but are very different from methane in polar character. The higher homologs of methane, C_2H_6, C_5H_{12}, C_6H_{14}, etc., should resemble methane, and not water or methyl alcohol, in dissolving other substances. The higher homologs, such as C_6H_{14} (hexane), are liquids, constituents of crude petroleum and gasoline. Oil (gasoline) and water do not mix. In chemical terms they do not mix since gasoline consists of nonpolar molecules, and water is a polar liquid.

If it is rational that water and methyl alcohol are both polar in character, then the complete miscibility of these two liquids is also rational. The R-group in an alcohol, however, is the same alkyl group that may be cited in an alkane.

$$R—H \qquad R—OH$$
alkane \qquad alcohol

As the R-group gets longer in an alcohol we might expect the resemblance to water to diminish and the resemblance to an alkane to increase.

$$CH_4 \qquad CH_3—CH_2—CH_2—CH_2—CH_2—CH_3$$
$$CH_3—OH \qquad CH_3—CH_2—CH_2—CH_2—CH_2—CH_2—OH$$
1-hexanol

Suppose that the functional group (OH) in an alcohol is the dog and the R-group is the tail. In methyl alcohol, CH_3OH, the dog may be said to wag the tail, but in 1-hexanol, the tail begins to wag the dog in the structural formula. The analogy is pertinent to the solubility of alcohols in water. Methyl alcohol, in which the OH group is a significant part (the dog wags the tail), is completely miscible with water, but 1-hexanol dissolves only to the extent of 0.6 g per 100 g of water (Table 2.4), suggesting that the tail now wags the dog. The longer group makes the molecule more like an alkane (R—H) and less like water (H—OH). When R is still longer—for example in $C_{18}H_{37}OH$—the alkyl group overshadows the functional group still more and the solubility in water diminishes almost to zero, scarcely more than that of an alkane itself. In a molecular model of $C_{18}H_{37}OH$, the dog is scarcely visible because of the bushy tail (Fig. 2.6).

FIGURE 2.6　*A ball-and-stick model of* $C_{18}H_{37}OH$ *showing how the alkyl group overshadows the functional group.*

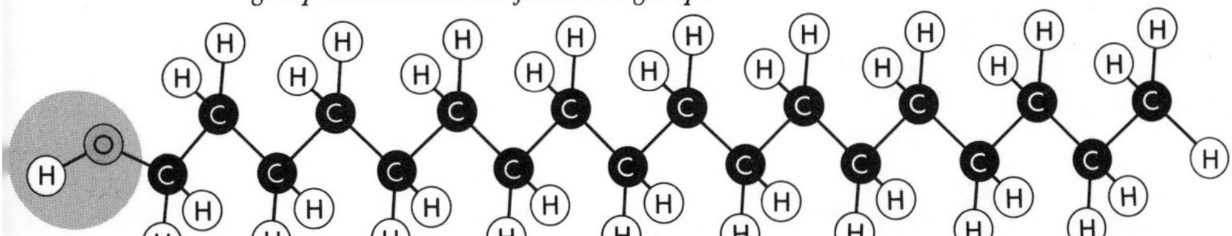

Exercise 2.2. Which solvent would you expect to be more suitable for dissolving
a. an oil spot: CCl_4 or CH_3OH?
b. sodium chloride: CCl_4 or HOH?
Give a reason for your answer, based on polarities.

Density of Water and Alcohols

Besides solubility and boiling point, a third macroscopic property of alcohols varies in a predictable way with increasing length of the R-group. The density of methanol (Table 2.4) is approximately 0.8 g/ml. The next two members of the series (Table 2.4) have nearly the same density, and then slowly the density of the liquid 1-ols climbs to 0.831 g/ml for 1-dodecanol. Although the 12 alcohols vary in density only from 0.792 to 0.831 g/ml, the change is a regular one with a small increment. The same is true for the related series of iso-alcohols (Table 2.4), beginning with 2-propanol ($d =$ 0.785 g/ml) to 5-methyl-1-hexanol ($d = 0.831$ g/ml).

We would not necessarily expect to predict relative densities of water, the 1-ols, and the iso-alcohols without a close study of the structure of the liquids. The individual molecules differ considerably in their shapes: water is a V-shaped, two-dimensional molecule (Fig. 2.4); the 1-ols have a three-dimensional structure with the functional group on one end (Fig. 1.4); and the iso-alcohols have a branch on the end opposite to the functional group. How they pack in the solid state and how much loosening up of this structure occurs when the crystal melts cannot be predicted from a cursory glance at the overall shape (Figs. 2.4 and 1.4).

Interatomic and intermolecular distances as well as bond angles would be essential to this examination before any relationship between structure and density could be established.

Reactions of Water and Alcohols

In the discussion of boiling points, densities, and solubilities of alcohols, we see some regularities. The boiling points of alcohols increase gradually as the molecular mass increases. The solubilities of alcohols in water also follow a predictable pattern, this time a decrease in solubility with increase in molecular mass. The density of members of a series of straight chain alcohols increases gradually. In these three properties, then, alcohols conform to the third part of the definition of homologous series (page 8): they have boiling points, densities, and solubilities varying in a regular manner.

Now we are ready to turn to the second part of the definition of homologous series (page 8) to see if the alcohols have similar chemical properties. We also will compare the chemical properties of alcohols with water to see if the OH group acts as a functional group in that compound, too.

In the next sections, six chemical reactions of water and alcohols are discussed: with metals, calcium chloride, hydrochloric acid, sulfuric acid, phosphorus halides, and covalent oxyhalides. Two closely related reactions characteristic only of alcohols (and phenols) are discussed: ether formation and esterification.

Metals with Water and Alcohols

Water reacts violently with the alkali metals to liberate hydrogen. Hydrogen is displaced; one hydrogen-oxygen bond is broken, leaving the other intact. Since water is commonly in large excess as the reaction is carried out, the question of whether the second hydrogen could be displaced does not arise. With a piece of sodium the reaction at the surface evolves enough heat to melt the sodium, and it dances around on the surface until it is consumed. Potassium reacts somewhat more vigorously, often setting the hydrogen on fire. The other alkali metals (lithium, rubidium, and cesium) also liberate hydrogen rapidly from water. The equations are analogous to Eqs. 2.1 and 2.2.

$$Na_{(s)} + H\!-\!OH_{(l)} \longrightarrow Na^+_{(aq)} + OH^-_{(aq)} + \tfrac{1}{2} H_{2(g)} \qquad \text{(Eq. 2.1)}$$
sodium hydroxide

$$K_{(s)} + H\!-\!OH_{(l)} \longrightarrow K^+_{(aq)} + OH^-_{(aq)} + \tfrac{1}{2} H_{2(g)} \qquad \text{(Eq. 2.2)}$$
potassium hydroxide

Since an alcohol, ROH, also bears a hydrogen-oxygen bond, displacement of hydrogen might be expected with the alkali metals. The short-chain alcohols, methyl and ethyl, for example, appear to react with the same initial vigor as water.

$$Na_{(s)} + H\!-\!OR_{(l)} \longrightarrow Na^+_{(alc)} + OR^-_{(alc)} + \tfrac{1}{2} H_{2(g)} \qquad \text{(Eq. 2.3)}$$

The NaOR, however, is less soluble in the alcohol than NaOH is in water and a coating of the NaOR on the sodium seems to slow up the reaction in a short time. It would be interesting to determine in an inert solvent whether the rate of reaction between water and sodium is indeed any faster than the reaction with an alcohol. The comparison of relative reactivity of water and alcohols with alkali metals appears not to have been made in any way except by visual observation.

As the molecular mass of the alcohol increases, the vigor of the reaction with sodium seems to diminish, but this may be a concentration effect since the alcoholic functional group would occupy a smaller fraction of the surface of the alcohol molecule. (This view implies that the sodium atom must come near the OH group to react, but this is only a reasonable assumption.) With the four-carbon alcohol, tert-butyl, the alcohol must be held at its boiling point in order for it to react completely with potassium in a reasonable time. Solid alcohols must be melted to get appreciable reaction with a metal, since surface contact is so small between two solids and the reaction rate is limited by rates of diffusion. The three-dimensional equation (below Eq. 2.4) gives an idea of the surface area on which the potassium atom must act.

$$K_{(s)} + (CH_3)_3COH_{(l)} \longrightarrow (CH_3)_3CO^-K^+_{(alc)} + \tfrac{1}{2} H_{2(g)} \qquad \text{(Eq. 2.4)}$$

In analogy to potassium hydroxide, the product containing potassium in the alcohol case is called a *potassium alkoxide*. With the four-carbon alcohol, *tert*-butyl, the *yl* ending is dropped and -oxide is added to give the name, potassium *tert*-butoxide.

Exercise 2.3. Using condensed structural formulas, write equations for the reactions indicated:

Na + 2-butanol

Li + 1-propanol

K + 1-octanol

Exercise 2.4. Name the alkoxides formed in Exercise 2.3.

Exercise 2.5. Sodium metal does not react with diethyl ether, C_2H_5—O—C_2H_5. Suggest a test that might reveal whether a bottle of ether contains any water dissolved in it. What would you look for in the test?

Reactions with Calcium Chloride and Other Salts

Calcium chloride is a mild drying agent not nearly so efficient as others. In Table 2.5 the practical limits of water removal from air are given for four drying agents. In describing it as a drying agent, we mean that calcium chloride will remove water from air (or from liquids in which calcium chloride is insoluble). The water comes under the influence of the metal cation in the form of a complex. The calcium cation will complex up to six molecules of water (Eq. 2.5) in the form of an octahedral structure (Fig. 2.7).

$$\overset{++}{Ca}\overset{(-)}{(Cl)}_2 + 6H_2O \rightarrow [Ca(H_2O)_6]^{++}(Cl^-)_2 \qquad \text{(Eq. 2.5)}$$

Although the water may be driven off from the complex rather easily by heating, the complex is stable enough to remove water vapor from ordinary air at room temperature (Table 2.5). If at 100° air contained water vapor at equilibrium, the content would be approximately 18 grams per 22.4 liters. At 25°C, the vapor pressure of water is 23.7 mm. Therefore, at 25°C, the water content of air at equilibrium is

$$\frac{23.7}{760} \times \frac{18}{22.4} = 0.0246 \text{ g/l} \cong 2500 \times 10^{-5} \text{ g/l}$$

Somewhat less stable complexes are formed by calcium chloride with the alcohols of low molecular mass (Eq. 2.6).

$$CaCl_2 + 4 CH_3OH \longrightarrow [Ca(CH_3OH)_4]^{++}(Cl^-)_2 \qquad \text{(Eq. 2.6)}$$

Table 2.5 EFFICIENCY OF AIR-DRYING AGENTS AT 25°C

Air-drying agent	Water remaining per liter of air
$CaCl_2$	140×10^{-5} g
KOH	2×10^{-5} g
MgO	8×10^{-5} g
P_2O_5	0.001×10^{-5} g
None	2500×10^{-5} g

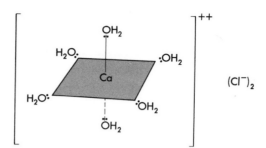

FIGURE 2.7 *The product of Eq. 2.5 in three-dimensional perspective.*

With higher alcohols, definite compounds cannot be identified, but no liquid alcohols can be dried with calcium chloride since it does react with both water and alcohols.

The complexes of water with salts are often called *hydrates*, and by analogy the alcohol complexes are called *alcoholates*.

A few other salts form alcoholates and hydrates. For example:

$$CuSO_4 + 5\ H_2O \longrightarrow CuSO_4 \cdot 5\ H_2O \qquad \text{(Eq. 2.7)}$$

$$CuSO_4 + 2\ CH_3OH \longrightarrow CuSO_4 \cdot 2\ CH_3OH \qquad \text{(Eq. 2.8)}$$

$$MgCl_2 + 6\ H_2O \longrightarrow MgCl_2 \cdot 6\ H_2O \qquad \text{(Eq. 2.9)}$$

$$MgCl_2 + 6\ CH_3OH \longrightarrow MgCl_2 \cdot 6\ CH_3OH \qquad \text{(Eq. 2.10)}$$

The size of the alcohol molecule determines the number that coordinates with the metal cation.

Reactions with Hydrochloric Acid

Hydrogen chloride is soluble in water to the extent of 503 volumes to one volume of water at $0°$ and one atmosphere of pressure. The reaction is exothermic to the extent of 18 kcal/mole at infinite dilution. The formation of the solution is accompanied by considerable interaction with the solvent, described by Eq. 2.11.

$$\underset{\text{acid}}{HCl} + \underset{\text{base}}{H\!:\!\overset{H}{\underset{\cdot\cdot}{O}}\!:} \longrightarrow \underset{+}{H\!:\!\overset{H}{\underset{\cdot\cdot}{O}}\!:\!H} + Cl^- \qquad \text{(Eq. 2.11)}$$

The reaction is an acid-base reaction, a proton being transferred from the acid, HCl, to the base, H_2O.

The acid strength (page 40) of HCl can be increased by forming a complex with some metal salts—for example, $ZnCl_2$.

$$HCl + ZnCl_2 \rightleftharpoons H^+[ZnCl_3]^- \qquad \text{(Eq. 2.12)}$$

An alcohol can behave in the same way as water with hydrogen chloride.

$$HCl + R\!:\!\overset{\cdot\cdot}{\underset{\cdot\cdot}{O}}\!:\!H \rightleftharpoons R\!:\!\overset{\cdot\cdot\oplus}{\underset{H}{O}}\!:\!H + Cl^{\ominus} \qquad \text{(Eq. 2.13)}$$

The reaction with water serves as a guide for writing the reaction with an alcohol. The alcohol is less basic than water and the equilibrium in Eq. 2.11

25

lies considerably farther to the right than that in Eq. 2.13 for the same (low) concentration of acid. However, the reaction with alcohol is complicated by the possibility of a second reaction to give a different set of products (Eq. 2.14).

$$\text{HCl} + \text{R}:\overset{..}{\text{O}}:\text{H} \longrightarrow \text{R}—\text{Cl} + \text{H}:\overset{..}{\text{O}}:\text{H} \qquad \text{(Eq. 2.14)}$$

This result is simply not available to the water-HCl reaction. It is to be noted that the net reaction of Eq. 2.14 may also be obtained by a reaction between products from Eq. 2.13.

$$\underset{\text{H}}{\overset{..\oplus}{\text{R}:\text{O}:\text{H}}} + \text{Cl}^{\ominus} \longrightarrow \text{R}—\text{Cl} + \text{HOH} \qquad \text{(Eq. 2.15)}$$

For further discussion, see page 36.

Reactions with Sulfuric Acid

Sulfuric acid dissolves in water in an exothermic reaction that is described in the same terms that we used on page 25 for the reaction of HCl and H_2O.

$$\overset{\text{base 1}}{\underset{..}{\text{H}:\overset{..}{\text{O}}:\text{H}}} + \overset{\text{acid 2}}{\text{H}:\text{OSO}_3\text{H}} \rightleftharpoons \overset{\text{acid 1}}{\underset{\text{H}}{\overset{..\oplus}{\text{H}:\text{O}:\text{H}}}} + \overset{\text{base 2}}{\overset{\ominus}{:\text{OSO}_3\text{H}}} \qquad \text{(Eq. 2.16)}$$

An alcohol can act as a base in the same way as water (Eq. 2.17) but again as in the alcohol-hydrochloric acid reaction additional net reactions are open to the alcohol-sulfuric acid system.

$$\underset{..}{\overset{..}{\text{R}:\text{O}:\text{H}}} + \text{H}:\text{OSO}_3\text{H} \rightleftharpoons \underset{\text{H}}{\overset{..\oplus}{\text{R}:\text{O}:\text{H}}} + \overset{\ominus}{:\text{OSO}_3\text{H}} \qquad \text{(Eq. 2.17a)}$$

The reaction described by Eq. 2.17a occurs rapidly and in dilute solution the products predominate. Upon warming, a second stage is reached (Eq. 2.17b).

$$\overset{\oplus}{\text{R}:\text{OH}_2} + \overset{\ominus}{:\text{OSO}_3\text{H}} \rightleftharpoons \text{R}:\text{OSO}_3\text{H} + \text{H}_2\text{O} \qquad \text{(Eq. 2.17b)}$$

The net result may also be described by Eq. 2.18.

$$\text{ROH} + \text{HOSO}_3\text{H} \longrightarrow \text{ROSO}_3\text{H} + \text{H}_2\text{O} \qquad \text{(Eq. 2.18)}$$

The product containing carbon, $ROSO_3H$, in Eq. 2.18 still has a hydrogen on oxygen and we might expect this hydrogen to be acidic.

The acidic hydrogen in $ROSO_3H$ may be neutralized by bases and an important use of these compounds stems from this possibility. When R is a long chain, for example, 12 carbons (Eq. 2.19), the neutralization of the alkyl hydrogen sulfate (Eq. 2.20) with sodium hydroxide gives a salt that can be used as a detergent.

$$CH_3(CH_2)_{10}CH_2OH + HOSO_3H \longrightarrow CH_3(CH_2)_{10}CH_2OSO_3H + H_2O$$

(Eq. 2.19)

$$\underset{\text{lauryl hydrogen sulfate}}{CH_3(CH_2)_{10}CH_2OSO_3H} + Na^+OH^- \longrightarrow \underset{\text{sodium lauryl sulfate}}{CH_3(CH_2)_{10}OSO_3^-Na^+} + H_2O$$

(Eq. 2.20)

The polar end of the salt, sodium lauryl sulfate, tends to make the compound soluble in water. The nonpolar alkyl chain tends to solubilize the compound in nonpolar solvents, such as oils. Solubility in both oil and water is the necessary requisite for an emulsifying agent, soap, or detergent. Sodium lauryl sulfate, then, is an agent for dispersing dirt (oily and greasy substances) in water. Such salts are the basis for one kind of compound used in the detergent industry. Sodium lauryl sulfate is sold under the trade names Dreft and Drene.

Reactions with Phosphorus Halides

Can the hydrolysis (reaction with water) of phosphorus trichloride, PCl_3, guide us to the behavior of PCl_3 with alcohols? Yes and no. The reaction with water is rapid and highly exothermic and thus a partial replacement of the halogens is impractical. Phosphorous acid is the only phosphorus moiety that has been identified in the sequence.

$$PCl_3 + 3 H_2O \longrightarrow \underset{\text{phosphorous acid}}{H-\overset{\displaystyle O}{\underset{\displaystyle OH}{P}}-OH} + 3 HCl$$

(Eq. 2.21)

The reaction of PCl_3 with alcohols is subject to better control and partial halogen replacement products have been isolated in several cases.

$$PCl_3 + CH_2{=}CH-CH_2OH \longrightarrow CH_2{=}CH-CH_2-O-\overset{\displaystyle Cl}{\underset{\displaystyle Cl}{P}} + HCl$$

(Eq. 2.22)

However, all three halogens may be displaced by OR groups. When PCl_3 is in excess, a monoalkyl product (Eq. 2.22) can be obtained, whereas a trialkyl phosphite is obtained, particularly if a trialkyl amine (R_3N) is added to take up the HCl (Eq. 2.23).

$$3 CH_3{-}CH_2{-}OH + PCl_3 + 3 R_3N \longrightarrow \underset{\text{triethyl phosphite}}{(CH_3CH_2O)_3P} + 3 R_3N{\cdot}HCl$$

(Eq. 2.23)

A speculative rationalization concerning the pathway that may be taken in arriving at these stoichiometric results is given in Exercise 2.10, p. 36.

Reactions with Covalent Oxyhalides

Phosphorus oxychloride is one of a series of compounds, known as *covalent oxyhalides*, that are formed by various elements from Groups IV, V, and VI (Table 2.6), as well as by a few other elements.

The reactions of all of these covalent oxyhalides with water and with alcohols may be treated as the chemistry of one functional group—namely, halogen attached to a central atom of relatively high electronegativity. The reaction with water is a displacement of the halogen by OH, such as was pictured for PCl_3 (Eq. 2.21). The reactions are exothermic and generally rapid among all of the compounds listed in Table 2.6. The hydrogen halide is liberated copiously.

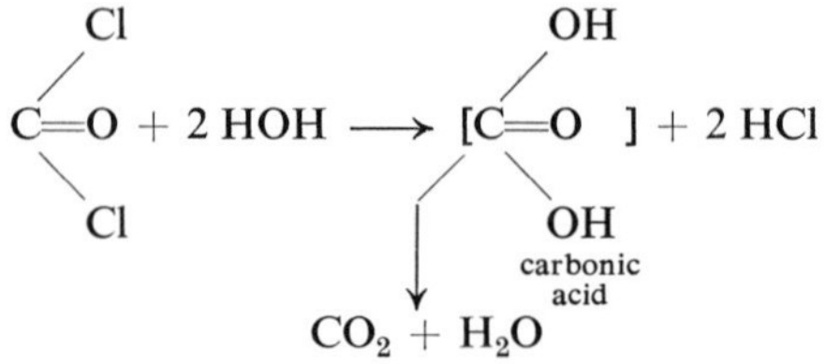

$$\underset{\overset{|}{Cl}}{\overset{Cl}{C}}\!\!=\!\!O + 2\,HOH \longrightarrow [\underset{\overset{|}{OH}}{\overset{OH}{C}}\!\!=\!\!O\ ] + 2\,HCl \qquad \text{(Eq. 2.24)}$$

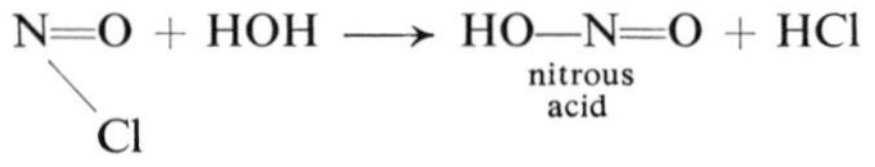

carbonic acid

$$\downarrow$$

$$CO_2 + H_2O$$

$$\underset{\overset{|}{Cl}}{N}\!\!=\!\!O + HOH \longrightarrow HO\!\!-\!\!N\!\!=\!\!O + HCl \qquad \text{(Eq. 2.25)}$$

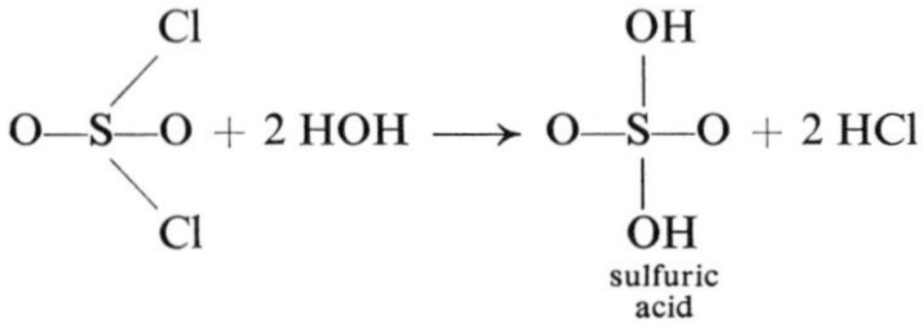

nitrous acid

$$O\!\!-\!\!\underset{\overset{|}{Cl}}{\overset{Cl}{S}}\!\!-\!\!O + 2\,HOH \longrightarrow O\!\!-\!\!\underset{\overset{|}{OH}}{\overset{OH}{S}}\!\!-\!\!O + 2\,HCl \qquad \text{(Eq. 2.26)}$$

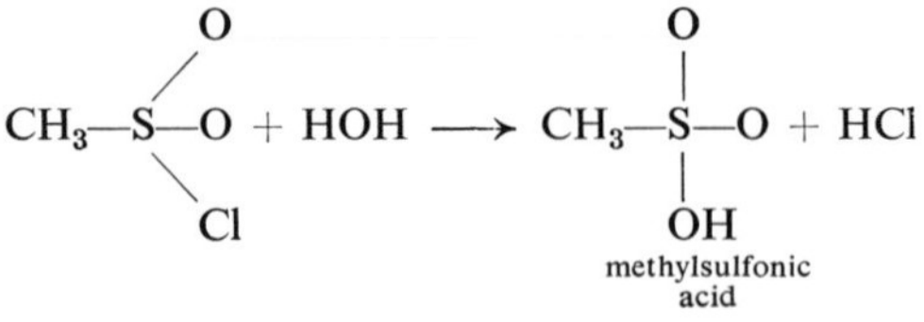

sulfuric acid

$$CH_3\!\!-\!\!\underset{\overset{|}{Cl}}{\overset{O}{S}}\!\!-\!\!O + HOH \longrightarrow CH_3\!\!-\!\!\underset{\overset{|}{OH}}{\overset{O}{S}}\!\!-\!\!O + HCl \qquad \text{(Eq. 2.27)}$$

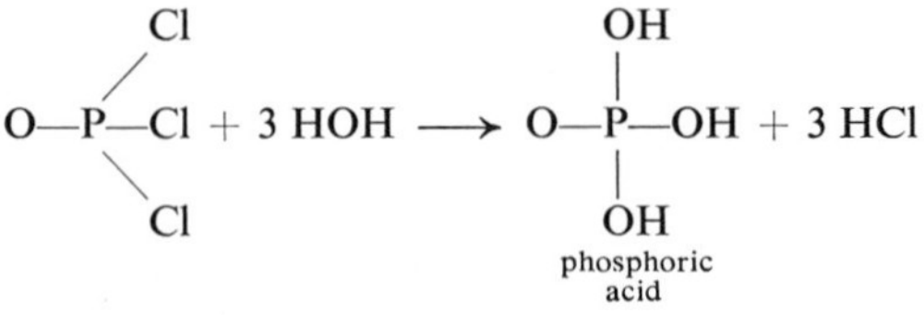

methylsulfonic acid

$$O\!\!-\!\!\underset{\overset{|}{Cl}}{\overset{Cl}{P}}\!\!-\!\!Cl + 3\,HOH \longrightarrow O\!\!-\!\!\underset{\overset{|}{OH}}{\overset{OH}{P}}\!\!-\!\!OH + 3\,HCl \qquad \text{(Eq. 2.28)}$$

phosphoric acid

Table 2.6 COVALENT OXYHALIDES

IV	bp	V	bp	VI	bp
$COCl_2$	8°	NOCl	−6°	$SOCl_2$	79°
$CH_3\!-\!COCl$	55°	$POCl_3$	105°	SO_2Cl_2	69°
		$VOCl_3$	127°	$CH_3\!-\!SO_2Cl$	160°
				$SeOCl_2$	176°
				CrO_2Cl_2	117°

None of these reactions is useful, since the products are easier to come by than are the starting compounds, but they are important because the reaction with water must be avoided in any useful reaction of the covalent oxyhalide. In the covalent oxyhalides containing more than one halogen, the reaction is so vigorous that hydrolysis of fewer than all the halogen atoms is impractical.

Alcohols react with covalent halides to displace halogens but two types of products are obtained in the net result (Exps.[3] 2.29 and 2.30).

$$
\begin{array}{ccc}
\text{OR} & \text{Cl} & \text{OH} \\
\diagup & \diagup & \diagup \\
\text{O--P--Cl + HCl} \xleftarrow{\text{ROH}} \text{O--P--Cl} \xrightarrow{\text{ROH}} \text{O--P--Cl + RCl} \\
\diagdown & \diagdown & \diagdown \\
\text{Cl} & \text{Cl} & \text{Cl}
\end{array}
$$

(Exp. 2.29)   (Exp. 2.30)

These competing reactions may be controlled to some extent. Adding a weak base, for example, will often promote the removal of HCl, favoring Exp. 2.29. The other halogens remaining on the phosphorus atom can, of course, exert the same function as the one shown in Exps. 2.29 and 2.30.

Exercise 2.6. Show all the products to be expected from mixing $COCl_2$ with CH_3—CH_2—OH. Which product might be favored if the reaction is carried out in the presence of a weak base?

Relative Acid Strengths

The equilibria described by the two equations 2.31 and 2.32 lie far to the right in dilute solution. We say that HCl and $HOSO_3H$ are strong acids.

$$HOH + HOSO_3H = H_3O^+ + {}^-OSO_3H \qquad \text{(Eq. 2.31)}$$

$$HOH + HCl = H_3O^+ + Cl^- \qquad \text{(Eq. 2.32)}$$

If the reactions both go essentially to completion in the direction indicated, then there is no difference in acid strength between these two acids in the solvent, water. However, by using a solvent that is a weaker base than water, these acids would have to work harder to transfer a proton to the new solvent, and might display a quantitative difference in behavior. In such a solvent, we might be able to determine the relative acid strength of these two acids or any series of strong acids which appear to have the same strength in water. One way to accomplish this is to choose a basic solvent that is a

---

[3] The term "Expression" (abbreviated "Exp.") will be used to describe a series of transformations or incomplete equations where some reactants or products are omitted.

very weak base indeed—namely, one that we ordinarily call *an acid in water solution*. Acetic acid would be such a weak base.

$$\underset{\text{base}_1}{CH_3-C\overset{O}{\underset{OH}{\diagdown}}} + \underset{\text{acid}_2}{HOSO_3H} = \underset{\text{acid}_1}{CH_3-C\overset{\overset{\oplus}{OH}}{\underset{OH}{\diagdown}}} + \underset{\text{base}_2}{\overset{\ominus}{O}SO_3H} \qquad \text{(Eq. 2.33)}$$

$$CH_3-C\overset{O}{\underset{OH}{\diagdown}} + HCl = CH_3-C\overset{\overset{\oplus}{OH}}{\underset{OH}{\diagdown}} + Cl^{\ominus} \qquad \text{(Eq. 2.34)}$$

In acetic acid, HCl is a better conductor of electricity than is the same concentration of sulfuric acid. This suggests that the equilibrium in Eq. 2.34 lies farther to the right than the equilibrium in Eq. 2.33, since increased conductivity must be due to increased numbers of ions. From this measurement and estimates of the strength of HCl from vapor pressure measurements we conclude that hydrochloric acid is a stronger acid than sulfuric. The K_a for HCl is about 10^7 while that of sulfuric is about 10^3.

In water, acetic acid is an acid, but acetic acid can be a base if it is made to behave that way by a stronger acid. Sulfuric and hydrochloric acids are capable of making acetic acid behave as a base. The environment determines the character of the OH group in the acetic acid molecule. This was one of the main ideas contributed to acid-base theory by Brönsted.

$$CH_3-C\overset{O}{\underset{\underset{HOH}{\big\downarrow}\quad OH}{\diagdown}} + HOSO_3H \rightleftharpoons CH_3-C\overset{O}{\underset{\overset{\oplus}{O}H}{\diagdown}} \rightleftharpoons CH_3-C\overset{\overset{\oplus}{OH}}{\underset{OH}{\diagdown}} + \overset{\ominus}{O}SO_3H$$

$$CH_3-C\overset{O}{\underset{O^{\ominus}}{\diagdown}} + H_3O^{\oplus} \qquad \text{(Exp. 2.35)}$$

The difference in behavior of acetic acid in the two solvents, water and methanol, indicates the difference in base strength of these two compounds. Acetic acid is about 10^5 times as strong an acid in water as it is in methanol, a less polar[4] and hence less basic solvent. Since two neutral molecules (CH_3COOH and solvent) go to two charged species (Exps. 2.36 and 2.37),

[4] With the same central atom (oxygen), water is more basic than methanol because it is more polar. In comparing molecules with different central atoms, the generalization cannot be made. Ammonia, for example, is a less polar molecule than water, but more basic. This time, the electronegativities of the central atoms (nitrogen and oxygen) are more significant than the polarities.

the more polar (basic) solvent (water) aids the proton transfer to a greater extent.

$$CH_3COOH + H_2O \rightleftharpoons CH_3COO^\ominus + H_3O^\oplus \qquad K_a = 1.8 \times 10^{-5}$$
$$\text{acid}_1 \qquad \text{base}_2 \qquad \text{base}_1 \qquad \text{acid}_2$$

(Exp. 2.36)

$$CH_3COOH + CH_3OH \rightleftharpoons CH_3COO^\ominus + CH_3\overset{\oplus}{O}H_2 \qquad K_a = 2. \times 10^{-10}$$
$$\text{acid}_1 \qquad \text{base}_2 \qquad \text{base}_1 \qquad \text{acid}_2$$

(Exp. 2.37)

The moral of this story, so to speak, is that the behavior of an OH group depends on its environment. In water, sulfuric acid has about the same strength as hydrochloric acid. In the weaker basic solvent (acetic acid), hydrochloric acid is a much stronger acid than sulfuric. In turn, acetic acid is a much stronger acid toward water (Exp. 2.36) than it is toward methanol (Exp. 2.37).

Esterification

When an alcohol (R'OH) and a carboxylic acid (R—C—OH) are allowed to come together in the presence of a small amount of a strong acid such as sulfuric, a product known as an *ester* is formed. For example, acetic acid and ethanol will react in what is called an *esterification reaction* to yield an ester (ethyl acetate) and water (Eq. 2.38).

$$CH_3-\overset{O}{\overset{\|}{C}}-OH + CH_3-CH_2-OH \underset{\longleftarrow}{\overset{HOSO_3H}{\longrightarrow}} CH_3-\overset{O}{\overset{\|}{C}}\overset{}{\underset{O-CH_2-CH_3}{\diagdown}} + H_2O$$

ethyl acetate
(an ester)

(Eq. 2.38)

With the sulfuric or other strong acid present, this equilibrium may be attained in a matter of days at room temperature or in a matter of hours at the boiling point of ethyl alcohol. The sulfuric acid does not change the position of equilibrium but only shortens the time of arriving there. Hence, sulfuric acid acts in the role of a catalyst. The equilibrium constant for ester formation for this particular pair of reactants is about 4.

$$K_{eq} = \frac{[CH_3COOCH_2CH_3][H_2O]}{[CH_3COOH][CH_3CH_2OH]} \cong 4 \qquad \text{(Eq. 2.39)}$$

Exercise 2.7. What is the maximum percentage yield of ethyl acetate obtainable from equimolar quantities of reactants from Eq. 2.38 if $K_{eq} = 4$ (Eq. 2.39)?

Exercise 2.8. What is the maximum percentage yield of ethyl acetate obtainable from 10 moles of acetic acid and one mole of ethanol at equilibrium, based on the ethanol?

Ethyl acetate, like other esters, is a sweet-smelling compound whose odor resembles that of banana oil. Indeed, a principal constituent of the odor of real bananas is the acetate ester of 3-methyl-1-butanol.

Esters of other oxyacids form an interesting group of compounds of widely different character and uses (Eqs. 2.40–2.43).

$$CH_3—CH_2—CH_2—CH_2—CH_2—OH + HONO \rightleftharpoons$$
$$CH_3—CH_2—CH_2—CH_2—CH_2—ONO + H_2O \quad (Eq. 2.40)$$

a nitrite ester
(a heart stimulant)

$$CH_3OH + HONO_2 \rightleftharpoons CH_3ONO_2 + H_2O \qquad (Eq. 2.41)$$

methyl nitrate
(an explosive)

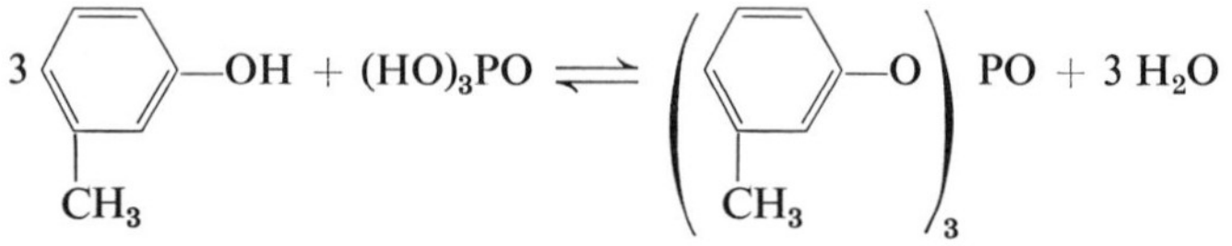

tricresyl phosphate
(TCP, a gasoline additive)

(Eq. 2.42)

$$C_{26}H_{53}OH + C_{25}H_{51}COOH \rightleftharpoons C_{25}H_{51}COOC_{26}H_{53} + H_2O$$

a constituent of
beeswax

(Eq. 2.43)

The reaction between an alcohol and sulfuric acid (Eqs. 2.18, 2.19) was an esterification reaction, although we did not name it at the time.

Ether Formation

Alcohols of low molecular mass dissolve in sulfuric acid and react to give alkyl hydrogen sulfates (Eq. 2.18), as is shown here with the example of ethyl alcohol (Eq. 2.44):

$$CH_3CH_2OH + HOSO_3H \rightleftharpoons CH_3CH_2OSO_3H + H_2O \quad (Eq. 2.44)$$

An equilibrium between the product ($CH_3CH_2OSO_3H$) and a second molecule of alcohol is not favorable for the formation of the dialkyl sulfate (Eq. 2.45) at low temperatures.

$$CH_3CH_2OSO_3H + CH_3CH_2OH \rightleftharpoons CH_3CH_2OSO_3CH_2CH_3 + H_2O$$

diethyl sulfate

(Eq. 2.45)

But if the pressure on the system is reduced and the temperature raised, diethyl sulfate distills away from the mixture, thus shifting the result to the formation of diethyl sulfate. Other acid-base equilibria are involved in the total picture but the two equations (2.44 and 2.45) represent the net reactions.

At temperatures of about 140° other equilibria are involved and the principal net reaction at this temperature with an excess of sulfuric acid is represented by Eq. 2.46.

$$2\ CH_3CH_2OH \xrightarrow{\text{HOSO}_3\text{H}} CH_3CH_2—O—CH_2CH_3 + H_2O \quad (Eq. 2.46)$$

diethyl ether

Reaction Pathways

In the six reactions of water and alcohols (pages 23–29) and the two reactions characteristic only of alcohols (pages 31 and 32) we have been concerned with net results. But chemists have shown some concern since 1900 for the pathway by which the net result obtains, and since about 1940 what is called *the mechanism of the reaction* has been of consuming interest. An inquiry into the reaction pathway or mechanism of a reaction can take varying degrees of sophistication; this can be illustrated by a more careful look at esterification (page 31).

A simple level of inquiry is to pose the question of the origin of water in the reaction (Eq. 2.47). Did the oxygen atom in the water come from the OH group in the acid or in the alcohol? Or does the oxygen in the water arise in random fashion from either source? This was determined experimentally by tagging the oxygen in the alcohol with excess O^{18} (beyond the percentage of O^{18} occurring naturally). The water formed in the reaction did not contain excess O^{18}. Therefore the source of water is that shown in boldface letters in Eq. 2.47.

$$CH_3-\overset{O}{\underset{OH}{C}} \quad + CH_3-CH_2-O^{18}H = CH_3-\overset{O}{\underset{O^{18}-CH_2CH_3}{C}} + \mathbf{H_2O}$$

(Eq. 2.47)

What role can we give to the sulfuric acid (a catalyst for the reaction, page 31), and how can we account for the oxygen in the product (water) arising from the acetic acid?

It would be logical to assume that the sulfuric acid might either protonate the alcoholic oxygen (Eq. 2.48) or an oxygen in the less basic acetic acid (Eq. 2.49; see also pages 29 and 30) in any mixture of the two.

$$CH_3-CH_2-OH + H^+ \rightleftharpoons CH_3-CH_2-\overset{\oplus}{\underset{H}{O}}H \qquad \text{(Eq. 2.48)}$$

$$CH_3-\overset{O}{\underset{OH}{C}} \quad + H^+ = CH_3-\overset{\overset{\oplus}{OH}}{\underset{OH}{C}} \qquad \text{(Eq. 2.49)}$$

But protonation of the alcoholic oxygen does not lead to the right result if the next step is loss of water from the conjugate acid of ethanol (Eq. 2.50).

$$CH_3-CH_2-\overset{\oplus}{\underset{H}{O}}H \longrightarrow CH_3-CH_2^{\oplus} + H_2O \qquad \text{(Eq. 2.50)}$$

Such a pathway should lead to $HO^{18}H$ (Eq. 2.47), but this is not observed. So, although protonation of the alcohol may occur (and undoubtedly does since ethanol is a stronger base than acetic acid), it does not lead to ester formation. The equilibrium of Eq. 2.48 is a spurious side-issue as far as the esterification reaction is concerned.

The following pathway will explain the results obtained at the bench (Exp. 2.51).

The protonation of acetic acid (*a* in Exp. 2.51) manifests itself in an electron-deficient carbon (*c*) which may be considered the source of attraction for the unshared pair of electrons on oxygen in the alcohol (*d*). A new bond (pair of dots) is formed in (*e*). It is to be noted that the oxygens marked 1 and 2 in (*e*) are now indistinguishable but oxygen 3 originated with the alcohol. A proton transfer from oxygen 3 to 2 (or 1) gives the intermediate (*f*) which can lose water, finally to yield ester through (*g*) and (*h*). This mechanism allows water to contain oxygen coming from the correct source (the acid *a*). The species (*a*) to (*h*) are written with an eye to making each step involve as small an energy change as possible. The steps preceding (*e*) merely involve proton transfers or a smearing-out of electrons. Step (*e*) involves the formation of the new C to O bond and may be the high-energy step, controlling the rate. Another possibility is that the bond-breaking step (*f* to *g*) may be the high-energy step.

It should not be inferred that these pictures exhaust the possible inter-mediate stages that may be written for this reaction; other pathways might be written to satisfy the original criteria set forth. We also should not infer that all other alcohols and all other acids necessarily follow a like path to esterification.[5]

Since an alcohol is a reactant in esterification reactions and water is a product, obviously the two compounds, water and alcohol, differ at least in degree if not in kind in their behavior in the equilibrium represented by Exp. 2.51. If the highest energy level in the reaction pathway is represented by (e) in Exp. 2.51, this level may be approached from either side if every step in Exp. 2.51 is reversible as we have indicated. In the approach to (e) from (g) and (f), water is playing the role of electron-pair donor to an electron-deficient carbon. In the approach to (e) from (c) and (d), the alcohol is playing the role of electron-pair donor to an electron-deficient carbon. In this most fundamental view, water and alcohol play the same role in the esterification and in the reverse, which is called *saponification*. From this standpoint, water and alcohols do not differ in kind of behavior, but only in degree.

The direction in which the reaction goes depends on concentrations, as is evident from Eq. 2.39. When the ratio of water to alcohol is low (for example, 1/10), then the ratio of ester to acid at equilibrium will be high (40/1); we say esterification predominates. When the ratio of water to alcohol is high (for example, 10/1), then the ratio of ester to acid at equilibrium is low (4/10), and the reverse reaction, saponification, predominates.

Esters are also formed with other oxyacids, although the pathway may not be that outlined for acetic acid and ethanol. Other esterifications are exemplified in Eqs. 2.40–2.43.

This does not end the inquiry into mechanism. Still more embarrassing questions can be asked about the pathway, and we need a check on as many of the intermediates (a) to (h) in Exp. 2.51 as we can get. Fragments (e) and (f) require sp^3 bonding on the central carbon (tetrahedral geometry), whereas this carbon in acetic acid has sp^2 bonding (flat, planar geometry). The product (ester) is again a flat, planar structure characterized by sp^2 bonding on the central carbon. Could an experiment be devised to test the interposition of a tetrahedral carbon between (a) and ester (Exp. 2.51)? For a discussion of this problem, see Gould.[5]

For a still more detailed picture of the mechanism we could ask about the bond length and bond angle changes at each step in the mechanism, the energy changes involved at each stage, and the rate at which each change occurs in the pathway. If you become a chemist, perhaps some day you will be able to contribute some answers to a still more sophisticated examination of the mechanism of esterification.

Exercise 2.9. With the assumption that the first step in the hydrolysis of PCl_3 is a proton transfer as shown,

$$PCl_3 + HOH \rightleftharpoons [H\overset{+}{P}Cl_3 {}^-OH]$$

write equations to show a possible pathway to the final product, $HPO(OH)_2$.

---

[5] See, for example, E. S. Gould, *Mechanism and Structure in Organic Chemistry*, Holt & Co., New York (1959), Ch. 9.

Exercise 2.10. With the assumption that the first step in the alcoholysis of PCl_3 is a proton transfer as shown,

$$PCl_3 + ROH \rightleftharpoons [H\overset{+}{P}Cl_3\,^-OR]$$

write equations to show a possible pathway to the final product, $P(OR)_3$.

Exercise 2.11. Sketch a three-dimensional picture of each intermediate, with phosphorus as the central atom, in each step of the pathway you have shown in Exercise 2.10.

Rate of Reaction of Alcohols with Hydrochloric Acid

Alkyl chlorides can be prepared by the action of hydrochloric acid on alcohols (page 25). Alkyl chlorides of all three types (Eqs. 2.52–2.54) can be made with concentrated hydrochloric acid, but the rate is slow with primary alcohols (Eq. 2.54):

$$R_3COH + HCl \rightleftharpoons R_3CCl + HOH \qquad \text{(Eq. 2.52)}$$
$$R_2CHOH + HCl \rightleftharpoons R_2CHCl + HOH \qquad \text{(Eq. 2.53)}$$
$$RCH_2OH + HCl \rightleftharpoons RCH_2Cl + HOH \qquad \text{(Eq. 2.54)}$$

The rate of the reaction of HCl with alcohols is greatly enhanced by increasing the acid strength of HCl with $ZnCl_2$. A solution of $ZnCl_2$ in concentrated HCl is used to distinguish among primary (RCH_2OH), secondary (R_2CHOH), and tertiary (R_3COH) alcohols. At 27°C, the rate of formation of R_3CCl (Eq. 2.52) is fast enough to give a milky precipitate of R_3CCl in less than a minute. The secondary alcohol forms the insoluble R_2CHCl (Eq. 2.53) within five minutes, but the primary alcohol does not react appreciably in the allotted time. At higher temperature the primary alcohols do react at an appreciable rate with $HCl + ZnCl_2$.

The faster reaction does not necessarily give the best yield. In the reaction of alcohols with hydrochloric acid containing $ZnCl_2$, the yield is generally better with the primary alcohol. The temperature is of necessity higher than room temperature, but the equilibrium at the elevated temperature favors product (primary alkyl chloride). In the case of secondary and tertiary alcohols, side reactions (particularly elimination of water to give alkenes) become more important, and the reaction is less favorable for the preparation of secondary and tertiary alkyl halides.

This example demonstrates the use of kinetic (rate) control versus equilibrium control in a chemical reaction. Use is made of the varying rates of reaction of primary, secondary, and tertiary alcohols with $HCl + ZnCl_2$ at 27°C to distinguish among the three types in a test tube. However, good yields of alkyl chlorides (equilibrium control) are obtained only with primary and secondary alcohols and the same reagent at elevated temperature in a reasonable time.

Exercise 2.12. Write equations for the reaction of 2-butanol with HCl. Why does $ZnCl_2$ act to catalyze this reaction?

Exercise 2.13. Explain what is meant by the statement, "The faster reaction does not necessarily give the best yield." (You will need to distinguish between equilibrium and reaction rate in your answer.)

Equilibria in Ether Formation

Alcohols react with sulfuric acid in various ways: to give esters (Eqs. 2.44 and 2.45), ethers (Eq. 2.46), and alkenes (discussed below). How can a chemist control a reaction, which takes at least four different pathways, to get the product he wants? First, the conditions for attaining each pathway must be studied carefully to see whether kinetic or equilibrium control is feasible.

We have already mentioned the methods of obtaining esters (page 31) and ethers (page 32).

When alcohol is in large excess so that sulfuric acid may be considered the solute and ethyl alcohol the solvent (as well as reactant), still other equilibria are involved (Eqs. 2.55–2.57):

$$CH_3CH_2OH + HOSO_3H \rightleftharpoons CH_3CH_2\overset{\oplus}{O}H_2 + \overset{\ominus}{O}SO_3H \quad \text{(Eq. 2.55)}$$
$$(a)$$

$$CH_3CH_2\overset{\oplus}{O}H_2 + CH_3CH_2OH \rightleftharpoons (CH_3CH_2)_2\overset{\oplus}{O}H + H_2O \quad \text{(Eq. 2.56)}$$
$$(a) \qquad\qquad\qquad\qquad (b)$$

$$(CH_3CH_2)_2\overset{\oplus}{O}H + CH_3CH_2OH \rightleftharpoons CH_3{-}CH_2{-}O{-}CH_2{-}CH_3 + CH_3CH_2\overset{\oplus}{O}H_2$$
$$(b) \qquad\qquad\qquad\qquad (c) \qquad\qquad\qquad (a)$$

$$\text{(Eq. 2.57)}$$

Optimum conditions for the formation of diethyl ether (c) are a temperature of 140° and a laboratory setup in which ethyl alcohol is added to the heated mixture of alcohol and sulfuric acid. The low boiling point of the ether (35°) results in its continuous removal from the system with concomitant disturbance of all equilibria (Eqs. 2.55–2.57). This can allow the production of about 12 moles of ether for one mole of sulfuric acid before the sulfuric acid is diluted sufficiently by the formation of water to make equilibria involving sulfuric acid and water predominate over the reaction involving sulfuric acid and alcohol. This practical limitation keeps the preparation of ether from being strictly a continuous process.

Again the roles of alcohol and water are similar in the reaction for ether formation (Eqs. 2.55–2.57). In this series the highest energy level in the pathway to an ether is probably reached in fragment (b) as the oxygen forms its third bond. In Eq. 2.56 the alcohol is an electron-pair donor to carbon in fragment (a). In the reverse reaction water is an electron-pair donor to carbon fragment (b). In this sense the ether formation reaction differs only in degree and not in kind from the esterification reaction (page 31).

At still higher temperatures (about 170°), the increase in the rate of formation of ether appears to lag behind the increase in the rate of another reaction which involves elimination of water from some of the positive fragments in the mixture (from a in Eqs. 2.55–2.57). At the elevated temperature, formation of the unsaturated compound $CH_2{=}CH_2$ predominates over ether

Table 2.7 REACTIONS OF WATER AND ETHANOL WITH THREE ACIDS

K_a	Acid	Conditions	H_2O	CH_3-CH_2-OH
10^7	HCl	25°	$H_3O^+ + Cl^-$	$CH_3CH_2\overset{\oplus}{O}H_2 + Cl^\ominus$
		reflux with $ZnCl_2$		$CH_3CH_2Cl + H_2O$
10^3	$HOSO_2OH$	25°	$H_3O^+ + \overset{-}{O}SO_3H$	$CH_3CH_2\overset{\oplus}{O}H_2 + \overset{\ominus}{O}SO_3H$
		warm		$CH_3CH_2OSO_3H + H_2O$
		warm, dilute		$CH_3CH_2OSO_3{}^\ominus + H_3O^\oplus$
		reduced pressure		$CH_3CH_2OSO_3CH_2CH_3 + H_2O$
		140°		$CH_3CH_2OCH_2CH_3 + H_2O$
		170°		$CH_2{=}CH_2 + H_2O$
1.8×10^{-5}	$CH_3-C\!\!\overset{\displaystyle O}{\underset{\displaystyle OH}{\diagup\hspace{-0.3em}\diagdown}}$	25°	$H_3O^+ + CH_3COO^-$	$CH_3CH_2\overset{\oplus}{O}H_2 + CH_3COO^\ominus$
		H_3O^+, reflux	—	$CH_3C\overset{\displaystyle O}{\overset{\diagup}{-}}OCH_2CH_3 + H_2O$

formation. Equation 2.58 is an example of an elimination reaction which may give rise to the unsaturated compound $CH_2{=}CH_2$.

$$CH_3-CH_2-\overset{\oplus}{O}H_2 + \overset{\ominus}{O}SO_3H \longrightarrow CH_2{=}CH_2 + H_2SO_4 + H_2O \quad \text{(Eq. 2.58)}$$

Water is one leaving group present in the mixture and $\overset{\ominus}{O}SO_3H$ is one base present that may accept a proton from the β-carbon in the positive fragment,

$$\overset{\beta}{C}H_3-\overset{\alpha}{C}H_2-\overset{\oplus}{O}H_2$$

or its successor,

$$\overset{\beta}{C}H_3\overset{\alpha}{C}H_2{}^\oplus$$

Alcohols, then, may form esters (e.g., alkyl hydrogen sulfates) with strong acids such as sulfuric, nitric, or phosphoric, or a molecule of water may be split out of each two molecules of alcohol to give an ether. The reagent is the same for both reactions, but changing the conditions allows one reaction to predominate over the other.

The reactions of water and ethanol with hydrochloric, sulfuric, and acetic acids are summarized in Table 2.7.

Comparison of Si—OH and C—OH Bonds

If water and alcohols have so many properties in common, could other elements be substituted for carbon and still maintain the properties of alcohols? The most promising answer might be sought first in substitution of an element from the same group in the periodic table. Could silicon, for example, be substituted for carbon in an alcohol, and still maintain the properties of an alcohol? The answer is no. Every element is unique. This is well demonstrated by comparing the properties of Si—OH and C—OH bonds. They have more differences than likenesses in common. The likenesses are of a formal nature.

1. Carbon cannot hold four OH groups on the same atom; silicon can. For example, $Si(OH)_4$ is known but $C(OH)_4$ is unknown.

2. As a corollary of statement 1, carbon is known to form double bonds with oxygen in both $>C{=}O$ and $-\overset{\displaystyle O}{\underset{OH}{\overset{\parallel}{C}}}-OH$ functions and rarely forms multiple OH bonds on the same carbon, $>\overset{OH}{\underset{}{C}}-OH$. Silicon is not known to form any silicon–oxygen double bonds except in the gas phase at high temperature, but may maintain two to four OH groups on the same silicon in wet reactions.

3. The Si—OH bond readily gives way to an ether-like linkage, Si—O—Si, while under similar conditions carbon more often forms $>C{=}O$.

$$\begin{array}{c} R \\ \diagdown \\ \underset{R}{\diagup}\ C\ \underset{OH}{\diagdown} \\ R\quad OH \end{array} \longrightarrow \begin{array}{c} R \\ \diagdown \\ C{=}O + HOH \\ \diagup \\ R \end{array} \qquad \text{(Eq. 2.59)}$$

$$\begin{array}{c} R \quad OH \\ \diagdown\ \diagup \\ Si \\ \diagup\ \diagdown \\ R \quad OH \end{array} \longrightarrow \begin{array}{c} R \\ | \\ -O{-}Si{-} + HOH \\ | \\ R \end{array} \qquad \text{(Eq. 2.60)}$$

Reasons for the generalizations made in this section and this chapter are correlated in the next chapter with electronegativity, size, and other factors influencing the character of bonds.

Summary

In this chapter we have emphasized the likenesses between water and alcohols in six reactions, and electron-pair donor abilities of the two in two other reactions which differ only in degree and not in kind. Alcohols undergo many reactions that do not have parallels in the reactions of water. We are leaving these for your future study in the field of organic chemistry.

Suggested Reference

Pimentel, G. C., and A. L. McClellan, *The Hydrogen Bond*, W. H. Freeman & Co., San Francisco (1959).

3

Influence

of the Neighborhood

on Properties

of the OH Group

As we saw in Chapter 1, the electronegativity of the atom adjacent to oxygen in the OH group may be used to estimate the gross character of the OH group. Metals in Groups I and II form strong bases with the OH group. Elements in Group VII—Cl, Br, I— form acidic compounds with the OH group, ClOH, BrOH, and IOH. Can we make any generalizations about the hydroxy compounds of the large number of elements within Groups III to VI that will be of practical value?

The elements of Groups III to VI form a large number of hydroxy compounds that fit into the general formula $(HO)_n MO_m$, where M is the central atom, n is the number of OH groups attached to the central atom M, and m is the number of oxygens unencumbered by any attached H or other atom. Not all known acidic substances fit into this formula, but a great many do.

As the chemist sees it, the strength of an acid is not the rate at which the acid disintegrates cloth, turns the skin brown, etches glass, or irritates the skin by dehydrating it. Instead, the chemist defines acid strength by the extent to which the acid donates a proton to water according to the equation

$$(HO)_n MO_m + HOH \rightleftharpoons$$
$$H_3O^+ + (HO)_{n-1} MO_{m+1}^-$$

If this equilibrium lies far to the right, the acid is said to be a strong acid.

40

How does the neighborhood around the central atom M affect the acid strength of $(HO)_n MO_m$?

Multiplicity of OH Groups

In the first place, the number of OH groups that can be supported about the central atom appears not to give any clue about acidic or basic strength. For example ClOH, $B(OH)_3$, $Ge(OH)_4$, and $Te(OH)_6$ are all very weak acids; HONO, $(HO)_2SeO$, and $(HO)_3PO$ are of intermediate acid strength; and $(HO)_2SO_2$ and $HONO_2$ are strong acids. In the general formula $(HO)_n MO_m$, all three classes of acids show various numerical values of n in common. The number of OH groups around the central atom is not in itself significant in determining acid strength, although the number of ionizations possible does, of course, depend on n.

Oxygen on the Central Atom

On the other hand, the number of unencumbered oxygens (m) on the central atom has a profound influence on acid strength. Pauling has suggested that each such oxygen increases the dissociation constant of an acid about 100,000 times (10^5).

Acid strengths are frequently compared in terms of pK's. If the first dissociation constant (K_1) for an acid $(HO)_n MO_m$ is defined by the following equations

$$(HO)_n MO_m \rightleftharpoons H^+ + (HO)_{n-1}MO_{m+1}^- \qquad \text{(Eq. 3.1)}$$

$$K_1 = \frac{[H^+][(HO)_{n-1}MO_{m+1}^-]}{[(HO)_n MO_m]} \qquad \text{(Eq. 3.2)}$$

then $pK_1 = -\log K_1$. For ionization of the second proton in the acid $(HO)_n MO_m$, the second ionization constant, K_2, is defined for the equation

$$(HO)_{n-1}MO_{m+1}^- \rightleftharpoons H^+ + (HO)_{n-2}MO_{m+2}^=$$

as

$$K_2 = \frac{[H^+][(HO)_{n-2}MO_{m+2}^=]}{[(HO)_{n-1}MO_{m+1}^-]}$$

and $pK_2 = -\log K_2$. K_3 and pK_3 have corresponding meanings. Pauling suggests that each excess oxygen not attached as an OH group to the central atom subtracts five pK units from the pK of a representative acid having no excess oxygen atoms on the central atom. This is a good working rule, as is shown in Table 3.1, although there are exceptions as might be expected from such a simple and empirical relationship. Any oxygen atom attached alone to the central atom seems to overpower the character of the central atom and dominate the scene as far as influence on acid strength is concerned. One excess oxygen atom on the central atom increases the dissociation constant of the acid enormously. The average pK for acids where $m = 0$ appears to be about 9 while for $m = 1$, the average pK appears to be approximately 3 and for $m = 2$, the average pK seems to be about -2.

Table 3.1 pK$_1$ FOR ACIDS OF FORMULA $(HO)_nMO_m$

$m = 0$	HOCl	7.2	Ga(OH)$_3$	10.3
	HOBr	8.7	Ge(OH)$_4$	8.6
	HOI	10.0	As(OH)$_3$	9.2
	Te(OH)$_6$	8.8	Si(OH)$_4$	9.7
$m = 1$	HOClO	2.0	(HO)$_3$PO	2.1
	(HO)$_5$IO	3.3	(HO)$_2$PO(H)	1.8
	(HO)$_2$SO	1.8	(HO)PO(H)$_2$	2.0
	(HO)$_2$SeO	2.6	(HO)$_2$PO(C$_6$H$_5$)	1.8
	(HO)$_2$TeO	2.7	(HO)$_2$PO(OCH$_3$)	1.5
	HONO	3.4	CH$_3$COOH	4.7
	(HO)$_2$CO	3.6(6.4)	HCOOH	3.8
	HOCN	3.9	(COOH)$_2$	1.2
	(HO)$_3$AsO	2.3	o-C$_6$H$_4$(COOH)$_2$	2.9
$m = 2$	(HO)$_2$SO$_2$	-3	HOClO$_2$	-1
	(HO)$_2$SeO$_2$	-3	HOIO$_2$	$+0.8$
	HONO$_2$	-1.6	(HO)$_2$CrO$_2$	-0.8
$m = 3$	HOClO$_3$	-8	HOMnO$_3$	-8

The first addition of an excess oxygen increases the acid strength by about 10^5 or 10^6. The second excess oxygen is only slightly less effective than the first. Only two examples (perchloric acid and permanganic acid) are known of the case where $m = 3$, and the pK of -8 for each is an estimate. The examples in Table 3.1 reveal both the differences between the groups in acid strength, and the approximate nature of the generalization.

When the unencumbered oxygens carry a negative charge, so that the acid corresponds to the ion formed in the first ionization of $(HO)_nMO_m$, the removal of a proton in the face of the negative charge is more difficult also by a factor of about 10^5. This is apparent from an examination of Tables 3.2a and 3.2b, where the pK$_2$ of the acid $(HO)_nMO_m$ (with $m = 1$) is not far removed from the pK$_1$ of the acid $(HO)_nMO_m$ (with $m = 0$; Table 3.1). The acid HOCl (pK $= 7.2$) has a strength comparable to that of an anion with

Table 3.2a pK$_2$ FOR ACIDS OF FORMULA $(HO)_nMO_m$

Anion$_1$				
$m = 1$	(HO)$_2$PO$_2$$^-$	7.2	(HO)SeO$_2$$^-$	7.3
	(HO)(H)PO$_2$$^-$	6.2	(HO)TeO$_2$$^-$	8.0
	(HO)$_2$AsO$_2$$^-$	7.0	(HO)$_4$IO$_2$$^-$	6.7
	(HO)SO$_2$$^-$	7.0	(HO)POOPO(OH)$^=$	7.3
Anion$_2$				
$m = 2$	HOSO$_3$$^-$	1.9	HOS(S)O$_2$$^-$	1.6
	HOSeO$_3$$^-$	2.1		

Table 3.2b pK$_3$ FOR ACIDS OF FORMULA $(HO)_nMO_m$

Anion$_2$				
$m = 1$	HOPO$_3$$^=$	12.4	(HO)$_3$IO$_3$$^=$	$\sim$15
	HOAsO$_3$$^=$	11.6		

42

a negative charge (-1) bearing two excess oxygens on the central atom, for example, $(HO)_2PO_2^-$:

$$
\begin{array}{ccc}
 & \text{OH} & \text{OH} \\
 & | & | \\
\text{HOCl} & \text{HO—P—O}^- & \text{HO—P—O} \\
 & | & | \\
 & \text{O} & \text{OH} \\
pK = 7.2 & pK = 7.2 & pK_1 = 2.1 \\
 & & pK_2 = 7.2
\end{array}
$$

The same phenomenon is exhibited by an individual acid carrying more than one OH group. For example, the pK_1 of $(HO)_3PO$ is 2.1, whereas the pK_2 of this acid is 7.2, five pK units higher. The pK_2 of $(HO)_3PO$ is equivalent to the pK of $(HO)_2PO_2^-$.

Adding another oxygen to the anion so that $m = 2$ now increases the acid strength by a factor of 10^5 again, as it did with K_1. For example, pK_2 for $(HO)_2SO_2$ is 1.9, whereas pK_2 for $(HO)_2SO$ is 7.0. The two selenium acids also exhibit a similar change in acid strength (Table 3.2a).

The numerical values of pK_3 are likewise increased by about five pK units. For example, pK_3 for $(HO)_3PO$ is 12.4, for $(HO)_5IO$ is about 15, and for $(HO)_3AsO$ is 11.6.

Replacement of Oxygen on the Central Atom

The replacement of an oxygen in the compound $(HO)_nMO_1$ by two hydrogens in the few examples that are known appears to add about 11 pK units to the dissociation constant of the acid (Table 3.3). In other words the acidic properties more or less vanish. In the case of the nitrogen acid HONO, the resulting compound, $HONH_2$, is indeed more prominent as a base than as an acid.[1] In the case of carbon the replacement of the carbonyl oxygen in the carboxylic acid by two H's converts the compound to an alcohol, after which the OH group is then essentially a neutral function. In the two examples of Table 3.3, methyl and ethyl alcohols have pK's about 11 units higher than the corresponding carboxylic acids.

Table 3.3 EFFECT ON pK OF REPLACING O IN $(HO)_nMO_m$ BY 2 H

HONO	3.4	HCOOH	3.8
$HONH_2$	~14	HCH_2OH	15.5
CH_3COOH	4.7	$HONO_2$	1.6
CH_3CH_2OH	15.8	$HO^-NH_4^+$	—
CF_3COOH	-0.2		
CF_3CH_2OH	12		

[1] The pK of 14 for NH_2OH was arrived at by extrapolating between $pK = 11.7$ for HOOH and $pK = 15.5$ for CH_3OH (Table 3.4):

$$H_2NOH \rightleftharpoons H_2NO^- + H^+$$

The ease of removal of the hydroxyl hydrogen in hydroxylamine has not been measured, but the pK should be between the limits of HOOH and CH_3OH from the position of the central atoms O, N, and C in the periodic table.

Changes in acid strength are less profound if at least one oxygen remains on the central atom—another manifestation of the incomparable effect of the oxygen atom. All replacements of OH groups in polyhydroxy acids, for example, are much less effective in changing acid strength than is the disappearance of an oxygen atom from the central atom. This can be shown in many examples, a few of which follow.

$$
\begin{array}{cccc}
\overset{\displaystyle O}{\underset{\displaystyle \|}{}} & \overset{\displaystyle O}{\underset{\displaystyle \|}{}} & \overset{\displaystyle O}{\underset{\displaystyle \|}{}} & \\
\text{HO—C—OH} & \text{H—C—OH} & \text{CH}_3\text{—C—OH} & \text{N}\!\equiv\!\text{C—OH} \\
\end{array}
$$

pK 3.6   3.8   4.7   3.9

If carbonic acid with pK 3.6 is taken as the starting point (see page 47, however), replacement of one OH by H to give formic acid, pK 3.8, does not make a profound change in acid strength. Likewise, the equivalent replacement of OH by CH_3 to give acetic acid, pK 4.7, makes a weaker acid by only about one pK unit. Perhaps it is a little more surprising that replacement of both OH and O in carbonic acid by the isoelectronic equivalent (N) to give cyanic acid (HO—C≡N) also diminishes the acid strength only slightly (pK 3.9). There is a big difference in the structure of the two acids, however (compare Chapter 6).

In the phosphorus acids also, replacement of an OH group by H (and replacement of two OH's by H's) or a carbon equivalent does not make large changes in acid strength, as the following examples from Table 3.1 show.

$$
\begin{array}{cccc}
\overset{\displaystyle O}{\underset{\displaystyle |}{}} & \overset{\displaystyle O}{\underset{\displaystyle |}{}} & \overset{\displaystyle O}{\underset{\displaystyle |}{}} & \overset{\displaystyle O}{\underset{\displaystyle |}{}} \\
\text{HO—P—OH} & \text{H—P—OH} & \text{H—P—OH} & \text{C}_6\text{H}_5\text{—P—OH} \\
\underset{\displaystyle |}{} & \underset{\displaystyle |}{} & \underset{\displaystyle |}{} & \underset{\displaystyle |}{} \\
\text{OH} & \text{OH} & \text{H} & \text{OH} \\
\end{array}
$$

pK 2.1   1.8   2.0   1.8

From the fact that hydrogen sulfide is more acidic than water we might conclude that sulfur with lower electronegativity adds more acidic character to a molecule than oxygen. However, replacement of oxygen by sulfur on a central atom is a different sort of change. Although there are few cases to examine, replacement of O by S in sulfuric acid has little effect on acidity, but that effect is in the direction of increased acidity. The first ionization constant of thiosulfuric acid has not been reported but the second is known. The two pK_2's are 1.9 and 1.6, respectively, nearly the same.

$$
\begin{array}{cc}
\text{HO}\quad\text{O} & \text{HO}\quad\text{S} \\
\diagdown\;\diagup & \diagdown\;\diagup \\
\text{S} & \text{S} \\
\diagup\;\diagdown & \diagup\;\diagdown \\
\text{HO}\quad\text{O} & \text{HO}\quad\text{O} \\
\end{array}
$$

pK_1 -3
pK_2 $+1.9$ $+1.6$

Since the electronegativities of S and O are quite different, this must mean that the availability of p_π orbitals in which to smear out a negative charge on the anion is more significant than electronegativity difference. Such orbitals are available on both S and O.

When the replacement of oxygen by sulfur gives an acid in which the return of a proton to the anion of the acid is not unequivocally to oxygen (Exp. 3.3), then we cannot say whether we are measuring the acidity of thiolacetic acid (4b) or thionacetic acid (4a).

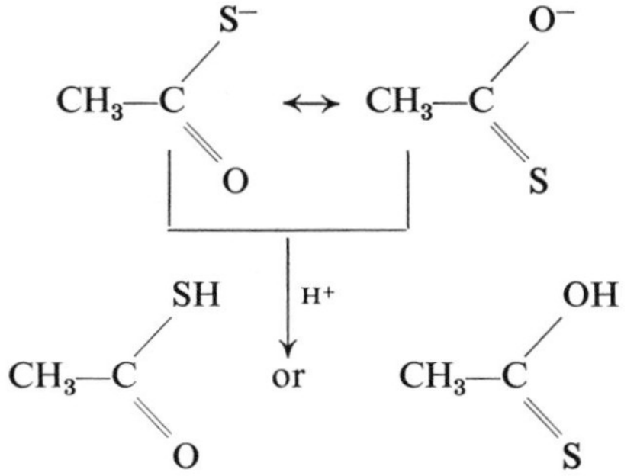

$$
\begin{array}{ccc}
 & S^- & O^- \\
CH_3-C & \longleftrightarrow & CH_3-C \\
 & \parallel & \parallel \\
 & O & S
\end{array}
$$

$$\Big\downarrow H^+$$ (Exp. 3.3)

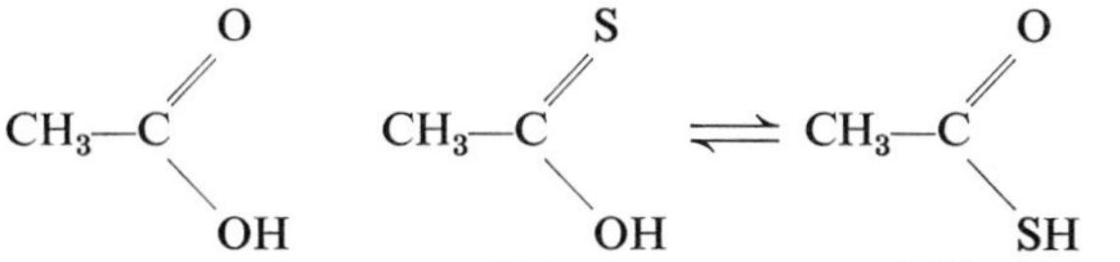

$$
\begin{array}{ccc}
SH & & OH \\
CH_3-C & \text{or} & CH_3-C \\
\parallel & & \parallel \\
O & & S
\end{array}
$$

$$
\begin{array}{ccc}
O & S & O \\
CH_3-C & CH_3-C \rightleftharpoons CH_3-C \\
\backslash & \backslash & \backslash \\
OH & OH & SH \\
 & (4a) & (4b)
\end{array}
$$ (Exp. 3.4)

pK   4.7   3.3

The anion of either (4a) or (4b) has a single structure (5a) and the return of the proton to the anion might give a mixture of (4a) and (4b) (Exp. 3.5). Thioacetic acid (pK 3.3), however, is a stronger acid than acetic (pK 4.7).

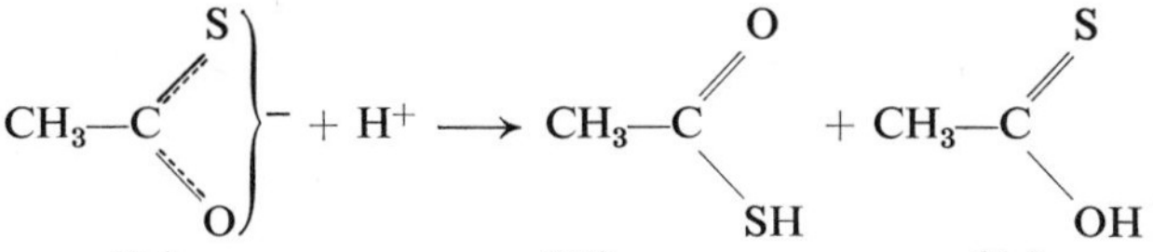

$$
\begin{array}{ccc}
S & O & S \\
CH_3-C \Big\}^- + H^+ \longrightarrow CH_3-C & + & CH_3-C \\
O & \backslash SH & \backslash OH \\
(5a) & (4b) & (4a)
\end{array}
$$ (Exp. 3.5)

Thiocyanic acid (6b) also is a much stronger acid than cyanic (6a) but now we are no longer considering acids of the formula $(HO)_n MO_m$.

$$
\begin{array}{ccc}
N\equiv C-OH & N\equiv C-SH & \text{(Exp. 3.6)} \\
\end{array}
$$

pK   3.9   -0.9
       (6a)   (6b)

Replacement of OH by atoms more electronegative than sulfur such as halogen also leads to strong acids but only two examples are known. Chlorosulfonic acid is a strong acid but cannot be used in aqueous solution since hydrolysis is very rapid.

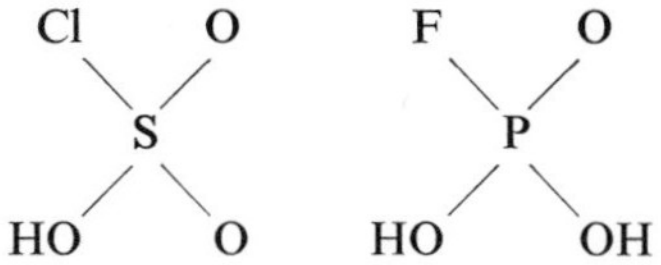

$$
\begin{array}{cc}
Cl \quad O & F \quad O \\
\diagdown \diagup & \diagdown \diagup \\
S & P \\
\diagup \diagdown & \diagup \diagdown \\
HO \quad O & HO \quad OH \\
\text{chlorosulfonic} & \text{fluorophosphonic} \\
\text{acid} & \text{acid}
\end{array}
$$

The corresponding fluorophosphonic acid does not hydrolyze rapidly but its pK_1 has not been reported. The pK_2 of fluorophosphonic acid (Table 3.4) of 5.1 suggests that pK_1 is probably less than 2 and hence fluorine may increase acid strength over that of the corresponding hydroxy acid ($pK_1 = 2.1$, Table 3.4). Judgment should be reserved on making any sweeping statement regarding the effect of a halogen substitution.

Replacement of OH by the corresponding nitrogen analog (NH_2, see Chapter 5) has two simultaneous effects. Since ammonia is basic by comparison with water, the introduction of the N analog of O might be expected to reduce acid strength.

Simultaneously, however, a change in structure is introduced since a "zwitterion" results. The word *zwitterion* refers to an inner salt or dipolar ion in which there is a charge separation between two parts of the same body—for example, structure 7b or 7d. Sulfamic acid, $HOSO_2NH_2$, is better described both in crystalline state and in solution by the zwitterion structure, 7b.

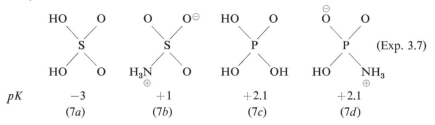

(Exp. 3.7)

pK -3 $+1$ $+2.1$ $+2.1$

(7a)   (7b)   (7c)   (7d)

Sulfamic acid is a strong acid in water solution and can, in fact, be used as a primary standard.[2] In contrast to the liquid mineral acids, sulfamic acid is a solid that can be manipulated by hand and even stored in cardboard cartons.

Phosphamic acid, 7d, is the corresponding substituted phosphoric acid (Table 3.4).

The NH_2 group appears to have a greater effect on acid strength in the S analog than it does in the P analog (Table 3.4), but to make any pronouncement on this aspect of substitution, we need the pK_2 of sulfamic acid, not now available.

Table 3.4 EFFECT ON pK OF ELECTRONEGATIVE GROUPS ON THE CENTRAL ATOM

			pK_1	pK_2	pK_3
$HOSO_2OH$	-3	$HOPO(OH)_2$	2.1	7.2	12.4
H_2NSO_2OH	$+1$	$H_2NPO(OH)_2$	2.1	3.8	10.3
$ClSO_2OH$	—	$FPO(OH)_2$	—	5.1	
		H—OH	15.7		
		CH_3—OH	15.5		
		H_2N—OH	~14		
		HO—OH	11.7		

[2] A primary standard acid is one that can be measured accurately to titrate against a solution of a base of unknown concentration. Accurate measurement is easily accomplished by weighing and most standard acids are solids, easily purified by recrystallization.

The action of base on sulfamic or phosphamic acid is, then, a removal of a proton from a zwitterion (Eq. 3.8), an internally charged species, and is not comparable to the removal of the first proton from neutral sulfuric (7a) or phosphoric (7c) acid. Whether the proton removed by the base is from N (as shown in Eq. 3.8) or from the remaining oxygen is not known.

$$
\overset{\ominus}{O} \quad O \qquad\qquad \overset{\ominus}{O} \quad O
$$
$$
P \quad + HO^- \longrightarrow \quad P \quad + H_2O \qquad \text{(Eq. 3.8)}
$$
$$
HO \quad \overset{\oplus}{NH_3} \qquad\qquad OH \quad NH_2
$$

The pK_1 of phosphamic acid was established by an equilibrium with HCl.

$$
\overset{\ominus}{O} \quad O \qquad\qquad HO \quad O
$$
$$
P \quad + HCl \rightleftharpoons \quad P \quad + Cl^- \qquad \text{(Eq. 3.9)}
$$
$$
HO \quad \overset{\oplus}{NH_3} \qquad\qquad HO \quad \overset{\oplus}{NH_3}
$$

The pK_2 and pK_3 numerical values are 3.8 and 10.3, respectively, and fall into line with those of phosphoric acid itself (Table 3.4). The pK_1 of sulfamic acid was determined in a different way.

Exercise 3.1. Write an equation for the hydrolysis of chlorosulfonic acid.

Exercise 3.2. Another acid which exists mainly as zwitterion is aminoacetic acid, $\overset{+}{H_3N}$—CH_2—COO^-. Write an equation for the reaction of this acid with aqueous sodium hydroxide. Would the zwitterion also react with a strong acid like HCl? Equation?

Size of the Adjacent Atom

In two acids where the central atom has the same electronegativity we may see the effect of size of the central atom.

$$
\begin{array}{cc}
HO & HO \\
\searrow & \searrow \\
C{=}O & S{=}O \\
\nearrow & \nearrow \\
HO & HO
\end{array}
$$

$$pK_1 = 3.6(6.4) \qquad pK_1 = 1.8$$

carbonic acid sulfurous acid

Carbon and sulfur have the same electronegativity (2.5) on the Pauling scale but the acid, sulfurous, with the larger central atom, is much stronger than carbonic acid. The pK's ordinarily given for these two acids, however, are somewhat deceptive since the acidic strength as commonly measured in water includes both hydrated $(HO)_2CO$ (Eq. 3.10b) and unhydrated (CO_2) (Eq. 3.10a) forms.[3]

$$XO_2 + H_2O \rightleftharpoons HOXO_2^- + H^+ \qquad\qquad \text{(Eq. 3.10}a\text{)}$$

$$(HO)_2XO \rightleftharpoons HOXO_2^- + H^+ \qquad\qquad \text{(Eq. 3.10}b\text{)}$$

If a correction is made for the fraction in unhydrated form, which is significant in the carbon case, the pK_1 is 3.6 rather than 6.4 (Table 3.1). The H_2SO_3 content of aqueous SO_2 (Eq. 3.10a) is so small as to be negligible. The molecular form H_2SO_3 is a strong acid and still significantly greater than that of the corrected figure for carbonic acid. The larger central atom in elements of the same electronegativity will give the stronger acid.

Influence of Structure on Acid Strength

In a strict sense, all the influences so far discussed have been structural in nature, but we now wish to turn to compounds with analogous molecular formulas wherein the difference is a gross difference in structure.

The importance of the factor of structure on acid strength is shown by two acids with analogous molecular formulas formed from central atoms of the same group (V) of the periodic table. Phosphorous acid (molecular formula H_3PO_3) and arsenious acid (molecular formula H_3AsO_3) have remarkably different acid strengths (Table 3.1). But when the correct structural formulas are shown, the great difference is more rational (Fig. 3.1). The structure of phosphorous acid makes it fit into formula $(HO)_nMO_m$, where $m = 1$ (except that there is also a P—H bond in the molecule). Phosphorous acid does have an acid strength that allows it to fall into the group of acids with one excess oxygen (Table 3.1), although arsenious acid falls into the lower end of the acid strengths of acids with no excess oxygens.

Acid Strength and Solvent Influences

Can we predict acid strength more precisely than is implied from the Pauling rules? With a series of closely related acids, can we predict the order of acid strength more precisely than five powers of 10 (10^5)? The answer is that we can do only a little better than that. There are too many gaps in our information about energy relationships and solvent properties.

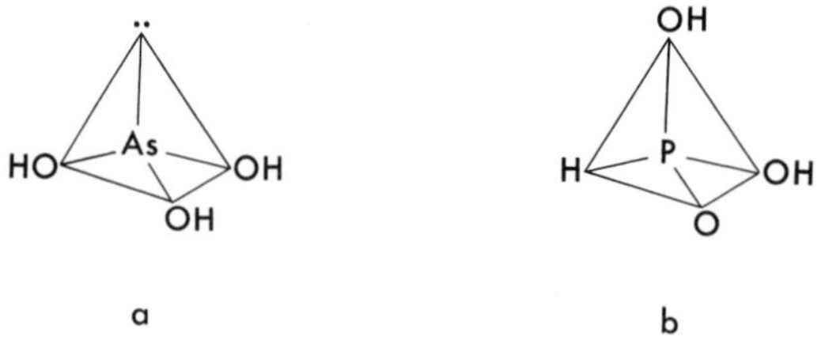

FIGURE 3.1 *Three-dimensional perspective of the tetrahedral structures of (a) arsenious acid and (b) phosphorous acid.*

[3] D. M. Kern, *J. Chem. Ed.*, **37**, 14 (1960).

One of the dark corners to be searched is the structure of liquids. Although we may know the precise geometry of molecular acids we do not know at all precisely what happens to these molecules in the presence of solvents. The main reason for the gaps in our knowledge in this area is lack of precise information about the cluster of solvent molecules around either the molecular acid or the ionic species. The thermodynamic functions that describe the properties of substances in the gas phase are often well known, but the corresponding properties of aqueous solutions are not. R. P. Bell[4] has very nicely pointed out this dilemma in a complete analysis of the acid strengths of the hydrohalogen acids, where the thermodynamic functions *are* known. Bell points out that this series of acids is the only one in which at present the information is complete.

It will be well to spell out this problem more carefully to see what energy relationships are involved in the quantitative determination of dissociation constants (K_a) in solution. The problem is considerably simpler with the hydrohalogen acids than with the hydroxy acids, since only two-atom molecules are involved.

The energy relationships can be divided into three parts: gas phase reactions, hydration steps, and dissociation energies in solution. Each part can be separated into steps, each of which carries an energy term. For example, the gas phase ionization of the hydrohalogen acids

$$HX_{(g)} \longrightarrow H^+_{(g)} + X^-_{(g)} \qquad \text{(Eq. 3.11)}$$

can be separated into three steps:

$$HX_{(g)} \longrightarrow H_{(g)} + X_{(g)} \qquad \Delta H_{\text{bond dissociation}} \qquad \text{(Exp. 3.12)}$$

$$H_{(g)} \longrightarrow H^+_{(g)} + e^- \qquad \Delta H_{\text{ionization of H}} \qquad \text{(Exp. 3.13)}$$

$$\underline{X_{(g)} + e^- \longrightarrow X^-_{(g)} \qquad \Delta H_{\text{electron affinity of X}} \qquad \text{(Exp. 3.14)}}$$

$$HX_{(g)} \longrightarrow H^+_{(g)} + X^-_{(g)} \qquad \Sigma \Delta H\text{'s} \qquad \text{(Exp. 3.11)}$$

The array of three equations (Exps. 3.12 to 3.14) and the summation (Exp. 3.11) and their associated ΔH's may be thought of as an energy cycle. The three ΔH's are measured in different ways and often the data for one of the three parts (most often the electron affinity, Exp. 3.14) are missing in the literature. By knowing three of the four ΔH's, then, the fourth may be calculated. Therefore, separating an overall reaction such as Exp. 3.13 into several parts is often useful in obtaining necessary information and understanding of the important factors.

These enthalpies (heats of reaction) for the four hydrohalogen acids are gathered in Table 3.5. The large positive numerical values for the ΔH's in the table mean that the gas phase ionizations are highly endothermic, and hence highly unfavorable except perhaps at very high temperatures.

[4] R. P. Bell, *The Proton in Chemistry*, Cornell University Press, Ithaca, N.Y. (1959), Ch. 7. Data for Tables 3.5 to 3.8 are from this source and are used by permission of the author and publisher.

Table 3.5 THERMODYNAMIC FUNCTIONS FOR GAS PHASE
DISSOCIATION OF HX AT $25°C$ (KCAL/MOLE)

	HF	HCl	HBr	HI
$\Delta H_{\text{bond dissociation}}$	135	103	88	71
$\Delta H_{\text{ionization of H}}$	315	315	315	315
$\Delta H_{\text{electron affinity of X}}$	-82	-87	-82	-76
$\Delta H^{\circ}_{\text{Exp. 3.11}}$	367	331	321	310
$T \Delta S^{\circ}$	7	7	7	7
ΔG°	360	324	314	303

We can speak more precisely in terms of free energies, ΔG°. If we assume that the entropy change ($T \Delta S^{\circ}$) for the four acids is nearly constant (7 kcal/mole), then we can calculate a standard free-energy change for these gas phase reactions from the relationship, $\Delta G^{\circ} = \Delta H^{\circ} - T \Delta S^{\circ}$. These numerical values are also gathered in Table 3.5.[5]

The large positive numerical values of each of the four free energies (ΔG°) tell us that the gas phase ionization is not feasible in the direction indicated (at $25°$). The decrease from HF to HI, however, means that acidity increases from HF to HI in the gas phase. The largest change is from HF to HCl.

In contrast, the hydration steps are highly exothermic. Although the enthalpy of hydration of the proton (Eq. 3.15) is somewhat uncertain, most recent calculations suggest a figure of -283 kcal/mole. Since the enthalpy of reaction (Eq. 3.16) of gaseous HX with water (at infinite dilution) can be measured in the laboratory, it is now possible to calculate the enthalpy of hydration of the anion (Eq. 3.17) by subtraction (Table 3.6).

$$H^{+}_{(g)} + H_2O_{(l)} \longrightarrow H^{+}_{(aq)} \qquad \text{(Eq. 3.15)}$$

$$HX_{(g)} + H_2O_{(l)} \longrightarrow H^{+}_{(aq)} + X^{-}_{(aq)} \qquad \text{(Eq. 3.16)}$$

$$X^{-}_{(g)} + H_2O_{(l)} \longrightarrow X^{-}_{(aq)} \qquad \text{(Eq. 3.17)}$$

The enthalpy connected with Equation 3.16 consists of two parts, the enthalpy of hydration of HX (Eq. 3.18) and the enthalpy of dissociation in solution (Eq. 3.19).

$$HX_{(g)} + H_2O_{(l)} \longrightarrow HX_{(aq)} \qquad \text{(Eq. 3.18)}$$

$$HX_{(aq)} \longrightarrow H^{+}_{(aq)} + X^{-}_{(aq)} \qquad \text{(Eq. 3.19)}$$

The contribution from the hydration of HX (Eq. 3.18) cannot be separated from the dissociation enthalpy (Eq. 3.19) and must be estimated from data

Table 3.6 ENTHALPIES OF HYDRATION OF HX AND IONS
AT $25°C$ (KCAL/MOLE)

	HF	HCl	HBr	HI
$\Delta H_{\text{Eq. 3.11}}$	367	331	321	310
$\Delta H_{\text{Eq. 3.15}}$	-283	-283	-283	-283
$\Delta H_{\text{Eq. 3.17}}$	-99	-66	-58	-47
$\Delta H_{\text{Eq. 3.16}}$	-15	-18	-20	-20

[5] All numerical values in Tables 3.5 to 3.8 are given in kilocalories per mole.

Table 3.7 ENTHALPIES OF HYDRATION AND DIS-
SOCIATION OF HX AT 25°C (KCAL/MOLE)

	HF	HCl	HBr	HI
$\Delta H^{\circ}_{\text{Eq. 3.18}}$	−12	−4	−5	−6
$\Delta H^{\circ}_{\text{Eq. 3.19}}$	−3	−14	−15	−14
$\Delta H^{\circ}_{\text{Eq. 3.16}}$	−15	−18	−20	−20

on molecules of similar size and polarity that do not dissociate. Estimates of
the division of these two enthalpies are shown in Table 3.7.

Finally, the three thermodynamic functions for dissociation in aqueous
solution are the numerical values we need to calculate an equilibrium constant for the dissociation of the acids in aqueous solution. These are given
in Table 3.8 where ΔH°_{aq} is $\Delta H_{\text{Eq. 3.19}}$ from Table 3.7. The numerical values
for the entropy terms $(T \Delta S_{aq})$ are estimates from the transfer of knowledge
about solvation of the anions in other systems. The standard free energy
relationship, $\Delta G^{\circ} = \Delta H^{\circ} - T \Delta S^{\circ}$, then gives the ΔG°_{aq} figures of Table 3.8.
From the additional relationship between free energy and equilibrium con-
stant (Eq. 3.20) the dissociation constants (given as $\log K_{\text{diss}}$ in Table 3.8)
for the hydrohalogen acids were calculated.

$$\Delta G^{\circ} = -RT \ln K = -1.36 \log K \qquad \text{(Eq. 3.20)}$$

Bell[6] points out that, in view of the several enthalpies and entropies
involved, it is fortuitous that the order of acid strength in aqueous solution
is the same as the order in the gas phase. He says, "This is one of the many
instances in which dissociation constants in water appear to reflect molecular
regularities more faithfully than might be anticipated."

The complete treatment of this series is given here to indicate to the reader
why we cannot yet rationalize the order of acid strengths of a series of acids
except in such closely related compounds as the hydrohalogen acids. In
general, the bond dissociation energies in the gas phase are known for most
acidic substances, but the electron affinities of the gaseous anions do not
make a long list. The entropies of hydration and dissociation in aqueous
solution cannot often even be reliably estimated because the extent of hydration is not known and the changes in entropy with changes in structure are
not known. Until such data are available, Pauling's simple generalization
relating acid strength to unencumbered oxygens on the central atom is the
best we have.

Table 3.8 DISSOCIATION IN AQUEOUS SOLUTION OF HX
AT 25°C (KCAL/MOLE)

	HF	HCl	HBr	HI
ΔH°_{aq}	−3	−14	−15	−14
$T \Delta S^{\circ}_{aq}$	−6	−4	−3	−1
ΔG°_{aq}	+3	−10	−12	−13
$\log K_{\text{diss}}$(calc)	−2	7	9	10
$\log K_{\text{diss}}$(obs)	−3	7	9	10

[6] R. P. Bell, *The Proton in Chemistry*, p. 92. Cornell University Press, Ithaca, N.Y. (1959).

Exercise 3.3. In each of the following pairs, which acid would you expect to be the stronger, and why?

    a. HONO and HOClO

    b. $(HO)_2P(H)O$ and $(HO)_3B$

    c. HOClO and $HOClO_2$

    d. $HOSO_2^-$ and $(HO)_2SO$

    e. CH_3—COOH and CH_3—SOOH

4

Condensations

between Molecules

Containing OH Groups

Examination of the formulas for molecules containing hydroxy groups as multiple functions attached to elements of the second and third rows of the periodic table suggests that under various circumstances the central atoms suffer from two types of condensations: *intramolecular* and *intermolecular atrophy*. Atrophy which is broadly interpreted as "degeneration through lack of nutrition," in this case refers to the loss of a molecule of water from the compound having hydroxy groups on the central atom (a condensation which may often be prevented by keeping the temperature low). Molecules lost by atrophy can often be restored by reaction of the dehydrated compound with water.

Nitrogen and Phosphorus Acids

As an example of intramolecular atrophy we may look at the possible formulas for acids of nitrogen (second row) and phosphorus (third row) as shown in Fig. 4.1. These formulas are based on the assumption that in oxidation state $+5$, each element might be capable of forming five bonds to OH groups. The plausibility of the assumption rests on the existence of compounds of phosphorus and halogens such as PF_5, PCl_5, PF_3Cl_2, and others. However, neither of the parent compounds

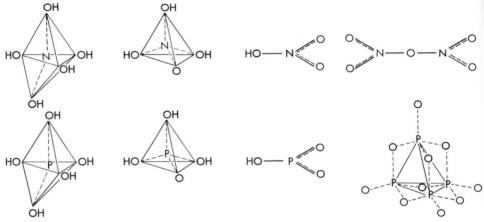

FIGURE 4.1 *Dehydration products of the unknown parent acids,* N(OH)$_5$ *and* P(OH)$_5$. [HOPO$_2$ *is unknown as such; only ring (trimer, Fig. 4.2) and chain polymer forms are known.*]

N(OH)$_5$ and P(OH)$_5$ is known, and no compounds of nitrogen are known with five groups on the nitrogen atom.

In Fig. 4.1, each succeeding formula on the right has lost the elements of water (atrophy within the molecule) from the preceding formula. Why should nitrogen in oxidation state $+5$ form only one nitric acid, HONO$_2$, and not (HO)$_3$NO or (HO)$_5$N? Why should phosphorus in oxidation state $+5$ form the stable, identifiable acids (HO)$_3$PO and HOPO$_2$ (as polymer), and by intermolecular atrophy

$$(HO)_2P(O)OP(O)(OH)OP(O)(OH)_2, \quad H_5P_3O_{10}$$

and others? In Fig. 4.1, the succession of compounds from left to right in each row are dehydration products. The final compound in the first row, N$_2$O$_5$, is an acid anhydride, the result of intermolecular dehydration of two molecules of nitric acid. It should be borne in mind that the "reactions" described are operations on conceptual models, and not necessarily reactions that can be performed at the bench. From right to left each compound should result from hydration or hydrolysis of the preceding compound. Old bonds are broken and new ones formed by taking up the elements of water.

In the laboratory, when water is added to N$_2$O$_5$, only one kind of nitric acid molecule (HONO$_2$) is formed, while by taking care it is possible to obtain (on the average) molecules of any of the three phosphoric acids (meta, ortho, and pyro; Figs. 4.1 and 4.2). Excess water tends to give orthophosphoric acid with P$_4$O$_{10}$, but never orthonitric acid with N$_2$O$_5$. Why should this be?

Phosphorus and Sulfur Acids

Like the nitrogen and phosphorus acids, the acids of phosphorus and sulfur differ in constitution. Sulfur forms a pyrosulfuric acid in "pure" sulfuric acid (in equilibrium with sulfuric acid) analogous to pyrophosphoric,

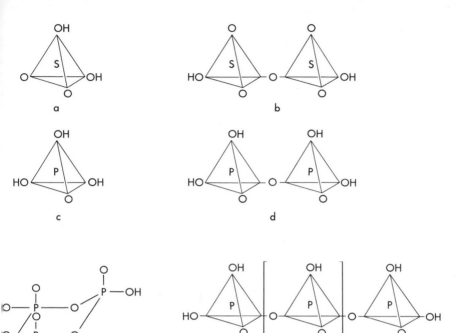

FIGURE 4.2 *Structures of (a) sulfuric acid; (b) pyrosulfuric acid; (c) orthophosphoric acid; (d) pyrophosphoric acid. (e) cyclotriphosphoric acid; (f) polyphosphoric acid*;*

but unlike phosphorus does not form an identifiable series of polyacids or any cyclic acids of the types shown for phosphorus in Fig. 4.2.

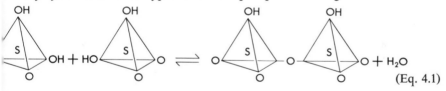

(Eq. 4.1)

Commercial grades of "oleum," containing 7%, 20%, 40%, or 65% SO_3 dissolved in sulfuric acid, are available. These fuming sulfuric acids may, however (even though not isolatable), be pictured as structural analogs of the polyphosphoric acids (Eq. 4.3).

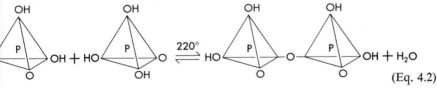

(Eq. 4.2)

* One polyphosphoric acid that can be purchased commercially carries the following analysis on the label:

H_3PO_4	5.7
$H_4P_2O_7$	21.4
$H_5P_3O_{10}$	18.0
$H_6P_4O_{13}$	13.4
Higher polyphosphoric acids	41.5
	100.0%

Intermolecular atrophy of water molecules in phosphoric acids (Eq. 4.2) gives a series of polyphosphoric acids which have definitely been identified up to a content of six phosphorus atoms (Eq. 4.3).

$$
\underset{\underset{\text{OH}}{|}}{\overset{\overset{\text{O}}{|}}{\text{HO—P—O—P—OH}}} + n \underset{\underset{\text{OH}}{|}}{\overset{\overset{\text{O}}{|}}{\text{HO—P—OH}}} \longrightarrow
$$

$$
\underset{\underset{\text{HO}}{|}}{\overset{\overset{\text{O}}{|}}{\text{HO—P}}} \left[\underset{\underset{\text{OH}}{|}}{\overset{\overset{\text{O}}{|}}{\text{—O—P}}} \right]_{n=1\text{-}4} \underset{\underset{\text{OH}}{|}}{\overset{\overset{\text{O}}{|}}{\text{—O—P—OH}}} + n\,H_2O \quad \text{(Eq. 4.3)}
$$

The tendency of phosphorus to form single P—O—P bonds in preference to P$=$O bonds with some double bond character (p_π-d_π) contrasts with the opposite tendency of nitrogen. Nitrogen forms double bonds to oxygen at every opportunity. Sulfur has an intermediate position, forming single S—O—S bonds in a limited number of cases with some fragile p_π-d_π character. Why should this be?

At the bench the loss of water can be accomplished by heating orthophosphoric acid to 220° (Eq. 4.2) to yield pyrophosphoric acid. At higher temperature (316° according to an 1833 report, and best carried out in a gold crucible!) either ortho- or pyrophosphoric acid yields metaphosphoric acid (Eq. 4.4).

$$
\underset{\underset{\text{OH}}{|}}{\overset{\overset{\text{O}}{|}}{\text{HO—P—OH}}} \xrightarrow{316°} \left(\text{HO—P} \overset{\overset{\displaystyle O}{\nearrow}}{\underset{\underset{\displaystyle O}{\searrow}}{}} \right)_n + H_2O \qquad \text{(Eq. 4.4)}
$$

The empirical formula, at least, is $HOPO_2$, although cyclic polymers, cyclotriphosphoric acid (Fig. 4.2e), and cyclotetraphosphoric acid, probably describe the molecular species. The formation of cyclic polymers again emphasizes the tendency of phosphorus to form stable single bonds to oxygen in P—O—P linkages.

The fundamental unit in all the phosphoric acids and their salts is the tetrahedral phosphorus atom joined to four oxygens. The tetrahedra are joined at oxygen either in rings or chains in which the bonding is P—O—P, P—O—H, or P$=$O.

It may well be emphasized that the difference in behavior of the sulfur and phosphorus acids is probably a case of kinetic control rather than thermodynamic stability. That is, more polyphosphoric acids have been identified than polysulfuric acids because the P—O—P bonds are slower to hydrolyze than S—O—S bonds. In a test tube, then, the chemist has time to identify P—O—P bonds but not time enough to verify the existence of S—O—S bonds. The conditions of liquid phase and room temperature for formation of the P—O—P bonds must therefore be favorable on the face of the evidence of identification of so many individual compounds. The polyphosphoric acids are most easily identified as their salts by chromatographic separation techniques. The separation and identification may be possible in the case of phosphorus and not in the case of sulfur simply because the S—O—S bond breaks faster in hydrolysis than the P—O—P, even though formation of an S—O—S bond may also be thermodynamically favorable (Eqs. 4.5 and 4.6).

$$2H^+ + S_2O_7^= + H_2O \xrightarrow{\text{rapid}} 2\,(HO)_2SO_2 \qquad \text{(Eq. 4.5)}$$

$$4H^+ + P_2O_7^{4-} + H_2O \xrightarrow{\text{slow}} 2\,(HO)_3PO \qquad \text{(Eq. 4.6)}$$

Whether this is a reasonable theory does not yet have an experimental answer. With techniques now available for studying fast reactions, an answer may be forthcoming.

The stability of the pyro and meta acids as compared with the ortho state depends on conditions. At sufficiently high acid concentration, the number of species in the S(VI) system may be as great as in the P(V) system, but a higher ratio of the acid anhydride to water is necessary to bring them out. Sulfur trioxide is known as a trimer $(SO_3)_3$ and a polymer $(SO_3)_n$. In glasses of the polymer with minute amounts of water present, a great variety of molecular structures may be possible.

The ease of formation and hydrolysis of P—O—P and C—O—P bonds at body temperature (37°) is significant in the synthesis of protein. In protein synthesis, the catalytic role of the nucleic acids RNA (ribose nucleic acid) and DNA (deoxyribose nucleic acid) and their building-blocks the nucleotides, such as AMP (adenosine monophosphate), ADP (adenosine diphosphate), and ATP (adenosine triphosphate), involves making and breaking phosphate diester linkages and pyrophosphate linkages.

The diester linkages are shown in a simplified picture of RNA (Fig. 4.3a). Pyrophosphate linkages (Fig. 4.3b) play a role in furnishing the driving force (free energy) in the complex coupled reactions involved in protein synthesis. Hydrolysis of the pyrophosphate P—O—P bonds is a source of driving force and energy release during the synthetic cycle. Details of the energy transfer are an unsolved and challenging problem in biochemistry. The approximate free energies (ΔG) involved in the reactions at pH 7 are given in Expressions 4.7 to 4.9.

$$\text{ATP} + H_2O \longrightarrow \text{ADP} + (HO)_3PO \qquad \Delta G = -8\ \text{kcal/mole} \qquad \text{(Exp. 4.7)}$$

$$\text{ADP} + H_2O \longrightarrow \text{AMP} + (HO)_3PO \qquad \Delta G = -6.5\ \text{kcal/mole} \qquad \text{(Exp. 4.8)}$$

$$\text{AMP} + H_2O \longrightarrow \text{adenosine} + (HO)_3PO \qquad \Delta G = -2.2\ \text{kcal/mole} \qquad \text{(Exp. 4.9)}$$

A comparison with the free energies of hydrolysis of a known phosphate ester,

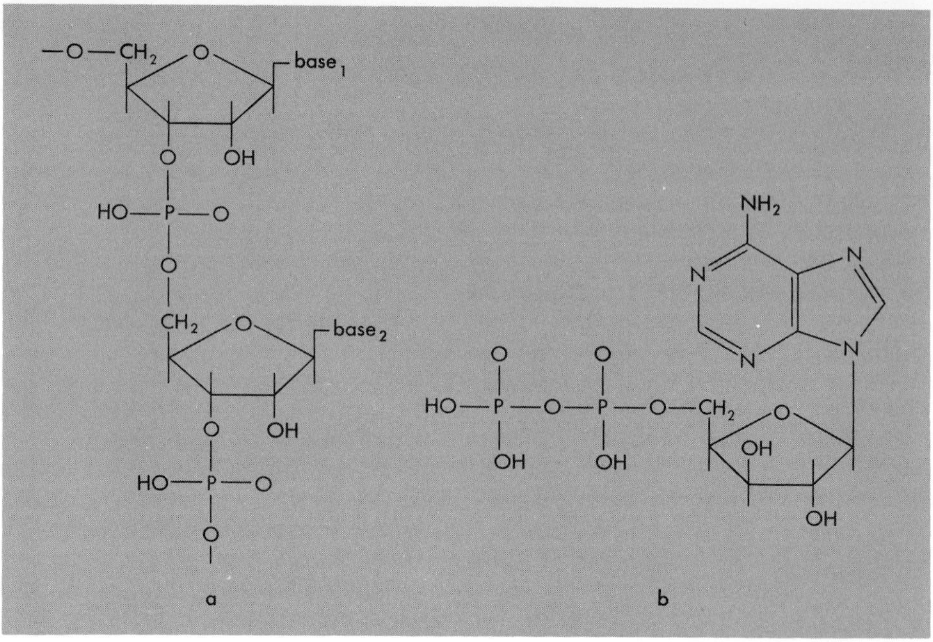

FIGURE 4.3 (a) *Two units in complex RNA (ribosenucleic acid) molecule showing phosphate diester bonds. Bases are purine derivatives.* (b) *ADP: Adenosine-5′-diphosphate.*

glucose-6-phosphate (Exp. 4.10) and a mixed anhydride (Exp. 4.11) are given for comparison.

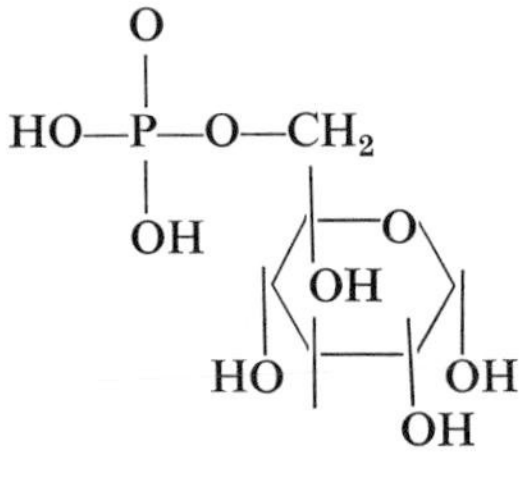

$$\text{glucose-6-phosphate} + H_2O \longrightarrow \text{glucose} + (HO)_3PO \qquad \text{(Exp. 4.10)}$$
$$\Delta G = -3.3 \text{ kcal/mole}$$

$$\underset{\substack{\text{acetic-phosphoric} \\ \text{anhydride}}}{CH_3\!-\!\overset{O}{\overset{\|}{C}}\!-\!O\!-\!\underset{\underset{OH}{|}}{\overset{O}{\overset{\|}{P}}}\!-\!OH} + H_2O \longrightarrow CH_3\!-\!\overset{O}{\overset{\|}{C}}\!-\!OH + (HO)_3PO \qquad \text{(Exp. 4.11)}$$
$$\Delta G = -10 \text{ kcal/mole}$$

Halogen Oxyacids

In the highest oxidation state of the halogens, $+7$, only chlorine and iodine form acids. Of these two elements forming acids, only periodic acid, $(HO)_5IO$, loses water to give an identifiable dimeric acid, $H_4I_2O_9$. At 80°, $H_4I_2O_9$ is formed from paraperiodic acid, while at 100°, the meta form of periodic acid predominates (Exp. 4.12).

$$(HO)_5IO \xrightarrow{80°} H_4I_2O_9 \xrightarrow{100°} HOIO_3 \qquad \text{(Exp. 4.12)}$$

58

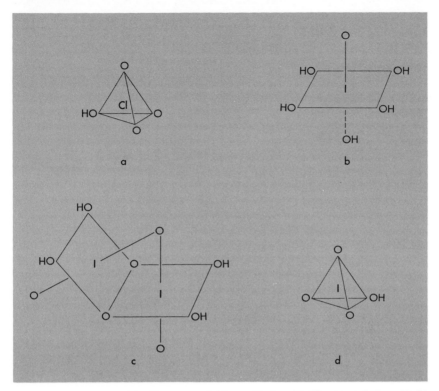

FIGURE 4.4   *Structures of (a) perchloric acid, (b) paraperiodic acid, (c)* $H_4I_2O_9$ *(conjectured), and (d) metaperiodic acid.*

The structure shown for $H_4I_2O_9$ (Fig. 4.4) is a conjecture, since that structure has apparently not been determined.

Carbon and Silicon Acids

From the existing compounds of carbon and silicon of Fig. 4.5, the conclusion might be drawn that carbon and silicon are unrelated elements, although silicon appears directly below carbon in the periodic table. Carbon apparently cannot hold four OH groups around itself in a stable structure, but forms multiple bonds to oxygen by atrophy of water molecules (e.g., carbon dioxide and carbonate salts). Silicon is not known to form multiple bonds to oxygen except perhaps in the unstable pyrophoric compound, SiO. The compound silicon dioxide, known in various forms, is always a polymer, $(SiO_2)_n$, in which there are four single bonds to oxygen. Each grain of white sand $(SiO_2)_n$ is probably one molecule!

Atrophy in C and Si Compounds

Proclivity toward multiple bond formation in carbon and lack of this tendency in silicon, has far-reaching consequences in the chemistry of carbon and silicon compounds containing OH functions. As an example, any attempt to synthesize a carbon compound with four, three, or two OH functions on the same carbon may be expected to end with carbon dioxide

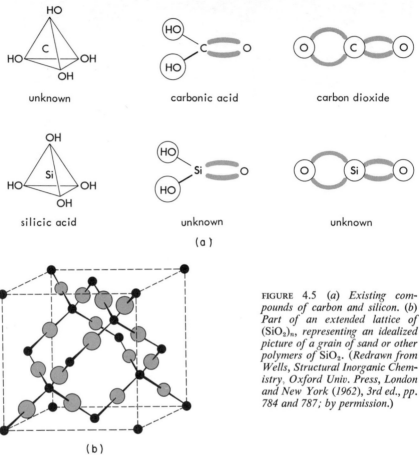

unknown   carbonic acid   carbon dioxide

silicic acid   unknown   unknown

(a)

(b)

FIGURE 4.5 (a) *Existing compounds of carbon and silicon.* (b) *Part of an extended lattice of* $(SiO_2)_n$, *representing an idealized picture of a grain of sand or other polymers of* SiO_2. (*Redrawn from Wells, Structural Inorganic Chemistry, Oxford Univ. Press, London and New York* (1962), *3rd ed., pp. 784 and 787; by permission.*)

(Eq. 4.13), a carboxylic acid (Eq. 4.14, where acetic acid is the example), or a carbonyl function instead (Eq. 4.15, where acetone is the example).

$$HO-\underset{\underset{OH}{|}}{\overset{\overset{OH}{|}}{C}}-OH \longrightarrow O{=}C{=}O + 2H_2O \qquad \text{(Eq. 4.13)}$$

$$CH_3-\underset{\underset{OH}{|}}{\overset{\overset{OH}{|}}{C}}-OH \longrightarrow CH_3-\overset{\overset{O}{\diagup}}{\underset{\diagdown OH}{C}} + H_2O \qquad \text{(Eq. 4.14)}$$

acetic acid

$$CH_3-\underset{\underset{OH}{|}}{\overset{\overset{OH}{|}}{C}}-CH_3 \longrightarrow CH_3-\underset{\underset{O}{\|}}{C}-CH_3 + H_2O \qquad \text{(Eq. 4.15)}$$

acetone

Two OH functions on carbon can be stabilized in a few unusual cases where electron-attracting atoms are piled up on carbon adjacent to the carbonyl function. For example, chloral is stable in the form of a hydrate which has the following structure.

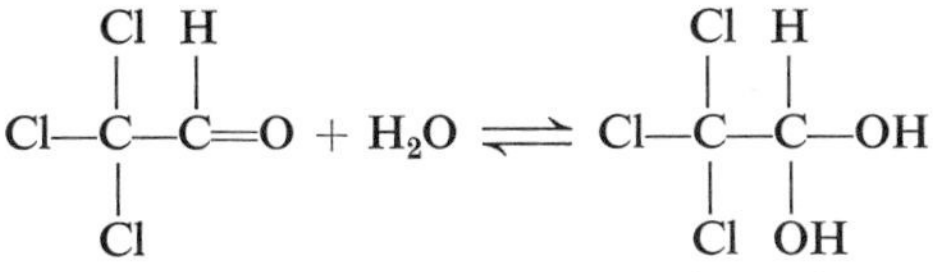

$$\underset{\substack{| \\ Cl \\ \text{chloral}}}{\overset{\substack{Cl\ \ H \\ |\ \ \ | \\}}{Cl-C-C}}=O + H_2O \rightleftharpoons \underset{\substack{| \ \ | \\ Cl\ \ OH \\ \text{chloral hydrate}}}{\overset{\substack{Cl\ \ H \\ |\ \ \ | \\}}{Cl-C-C}}-OH \qquad \text{(Eq. 4.16)}$$

The electron-attracting halogen atoms on the α carbon (adjacent to the carbon-carrying OH groups) make the carbonyl carbon sufficiently electron-deficient to attract another electron pair from oxygen in the water molecule and hold the two OH functions in stable bonds.

A carboxyl group (COOH) also is sufficiently electron-attracting to stabilize an adjacent carbonyl group so that the hydrated form (b) is the stable form (98%) of the acid (a) shown in Eq. 4.17.

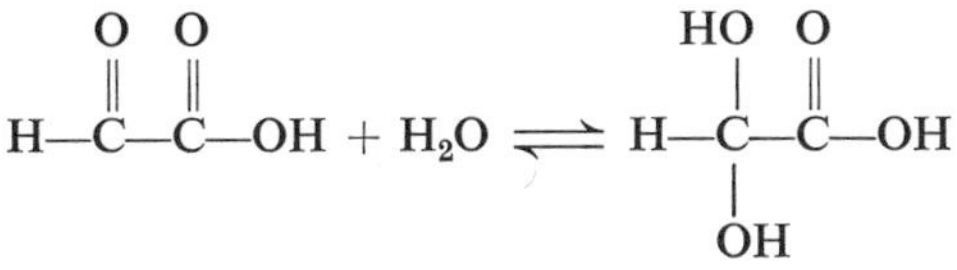

$$\underset{(a)}{\overset{\substack{O\ \ \ O \\ ||\ \ \ || \\}}{H-C-C}}-OH + H_2O \rightleftharpoons \underset{\substack{| \\ OH \\ (b)}}{\overset{\substack{HO\ \ O \\ |\ \ \ || \\}}{H-C-C}}-OH \qquad \text{(Eq. 4.17)}$$

Even the problem of polymerizing a carbonyl compound, formaldehyde,

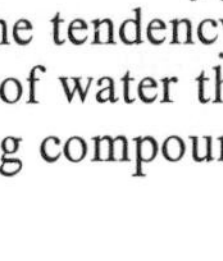

$$\overset{H}{\underset{H}{\diagdown\diagup}}C=O$$

formaldehyde

so that there are two single bonds to oxygen on each carbon in the chain (Eq. 4.18) has been plagued by the tendency of the polymer ($18b$) to become unzipped. By loss of a molecule of water the single bond functions revert to double bonds ($18a$) in the starting compound (reverse of Eq. 4.18).

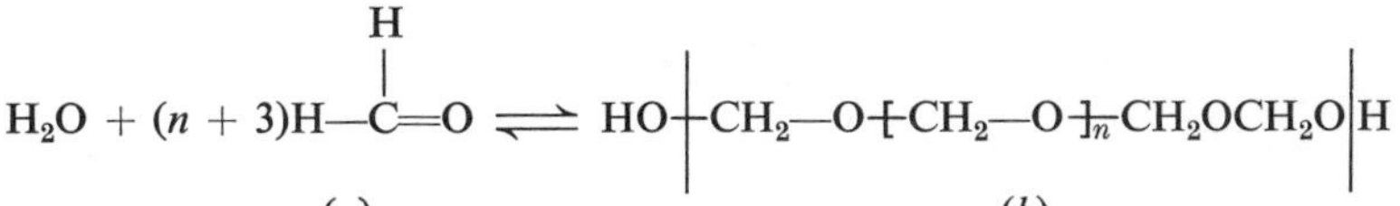

$$H_2O + (n+3)\overset{\overset{\textstyle H}{|}}{H-C}=O \rightleftharpoons \underset{(a)}{} HO\left[CH_2-O\left(CH_2-O\right)_n CH_2OCH_2O\right]H \underset{(b)}{}$$

$$\text{(Eq. 4.18)}$$

The chemical industry solved the problem of the reversal of the polymerization by placing a group (an ester group) on the end OH functions that would not so readily dissociate. Polymers of formaldehyde, of average molecular mass 150,000, can thus be stabilized in solids as a convenient source of formaldehyde.

By contrast to carbon, silicon always maintains single bonds to oxygen even when the possibility of double bond formation might seem favorable (Exp. 4.19). In any synthetic process where the chemist would expect in a carbon system to lose water to form a double bond (Eqs. 4.13 to 4.15), single bonds are invariably maintained in the corresponding silicon system. The silicone resins offer an example of maintenance of Si—O single bonds, the one best known to the public being "silly putty." If very pure dimethyldichlorosilane (19a) is hydrolyzed (Exp. 4.19), a long-chain polymer is formed which we can represent as an intermolecular atrophy of OH groups after the original displacement of halogen by OH. The resulting polymer (19b) has the peculiar property of allowing moderate stretching (like chewing gum) under gentle stress, but exhibiting brittleness (like cold taffy) under a sudden stress. The silicone polymer, "silly putty," can be rolled into a ball and will bounce like rubber, but upon standing it "lies down" and, like a viscous liquid, takes the shape of its container. There is nothing quite like it under the sun.

(Exp. 4.19)

With carbon as the central atom, we could expect by hydrolysis to obtain the corresponding carbonyl compound, acetone (Exp. 4.20), but the silicon analog (19c, Exp. 4.19) is unknown.

The loss of water in the silicon compound occurs intermolecularly (Exp. 4.19) rather than intramolecularly, in spite of the fact that intermolecular collisions would appear to have a lower probability of occurring than atrophy of OH groups within the molecule.

Hydrolysis of methyltrichlorosilane (CH_3—$SiCl_3$) does not give the silicon analog (21b) of acetic acid (Eq. 4.14) by intramolecular atrophy, but a polymer that has the possibility of cross-linking into a 3-dimensional network (Exp. 4.21 and Fig. 4.6).

$$
\begin{array}{ccccc}
\text{Cl} & & \text{OH} & & \text{O} \\
| & & | & & \diagup\!\!\!/ \\
CH_3\text{—Si—Cl} & \xrightarrow{H_2O} & CH_3\text{—Si—OH} & \xrightarrow{\;\;\;\;\;} & CH_3\text{—Si} \\
| & & | & & \diagdown \\
\text{Cl} & & \text{OH} & & \text{OH} \\
(21a) & & & & (21b)
\end{array}
$$

$$
\begin{array}{ccccc}
 & CH_3 & \left[\, CH_3 \,\right] & CH_3 & \\
 & | & \left[\; | \;\right] & | & \\
\text{HO—Si—O} & \!\!\!\text{—}\!\!\! & \text{Si—O} & \!\!\!\text{—}\!\!\!\text{Si—O—H} & \quad\text{(Exp. 4.21)} \\
 & | & \left[\; | \;\right]_n & | & \\
 & \text{OH} & \left[\, \text{OH} \,\right] & \text{OH} &
\end{array}
$$

$$(21c)$$

cross-linked polymer
(3-dimensional)

The propensity of silicon to surround itself with four oxygens in single bonds rather than with two oxygens in multiple bonds is demonstrated in the structures of several network solids of silicon. Quartz, of empirical formula SiO_2, is more properly portrayed as a polymer $[(SiO_2)_n]$ wherein every crystal may very well be a single molecule. Most white sand has the network structure of quartz.

Mineral silicates consist of polymeric silicate anions, which are: (1) chain-type, such as the pyroxenes (Fig. 4.7a), amphibole (Fig. 4.7b), and asbestos; (2) layer-type, such as vermiculite (Fig. 4.7c); or (3) a three-dimensional type, such as some of the aluminate-silicate minerals. In all these cases each silicon atom is tetrahedrally surrounded by four oxygen atoms.

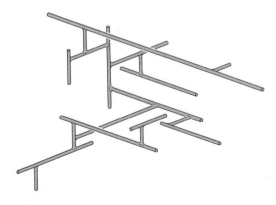

FIGURE 4.6 *A three-dimensional network polymer, cross-linked randomly.*

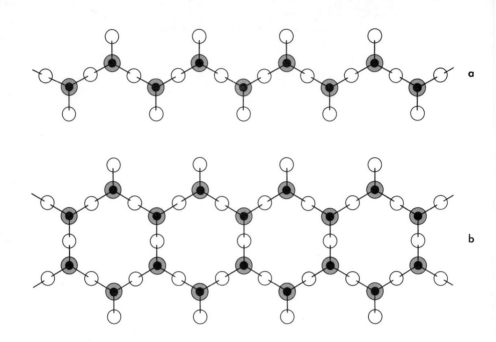

a

b

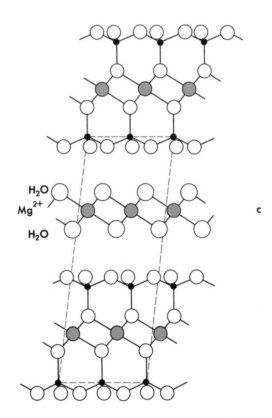

H₂O
Mg²⁺
H₂O

c

Ether Formation in C and Si Compounds

Silicon differs from carbon also in the lack of stability in the monohydroxy compounds. Whereas alcohols are not spontaneously converted into ethers but require acid catalysis and elevated temperature (page 37), the corresponding silanols themselves are difficult to isolate because of spontaneous intermolecular loss of water to give products analogous to ethers—for example, hexamethyldisiloxane.

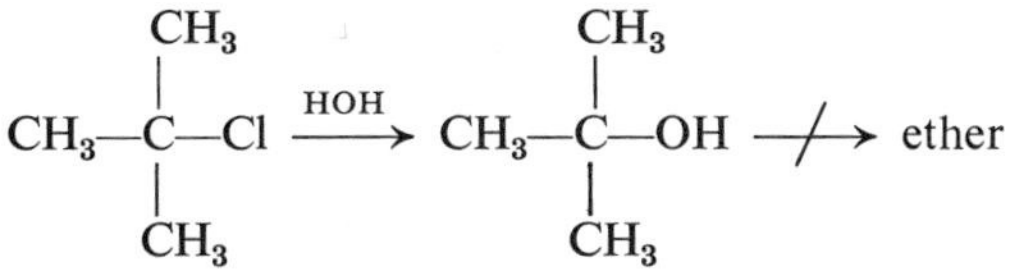

$$CH_3-\underset{\underset{CH_3}{|}}{\overset{\overset{CH_3}{|}}{C}}-Cl \xrightarrow{HOH} CH_3-\underset{\underset{CH_3}{|}}{\overset{\overset{CH_3}{|}}{C}}-OH \xrightarrow{\quad/\!\!\!\!\rightarrow\quad} ether \qquad (Exp. 4.22)$$

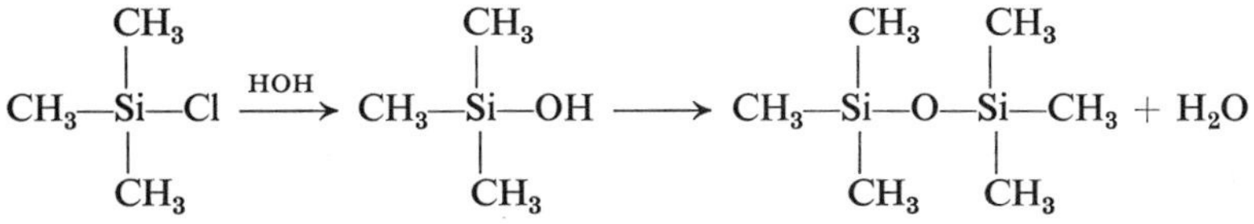

$$CH_3-\underset{\underset{CH_3}{|}}{\overset{\overset{CH_3}{|}}{Si}}-Cl \xrightarrow{HOH} CH_3-\underset{\underset{CH_3}{|}}{\overset{\overset{CH_3}{|}}{Si}}-OH \longrightarrow CH_3-\underset{\underset{CH_3}{|}}{\overset{\overset{CH_3}{|}}{Si}}-O-\underset{\underset{CH_3}{|}}{\overset{\overset{CH_3}{|}}{Si}}-CH_3 + H_2O$$

trimethylsilanol   hexamethyldisiloxane

(23a)

(Exp. 4.23)

If the hydrolysis medium is kept neutral, the intermediate silanol (23a) can be isolated, so the difference is only one of degree and not kind. The silanediols (Exp. 4.24) can also be isolated from hydrolysis of R_2SiCl_2 when R is C_2H_5, C_3H_7, or $n\text{-}C_4H_9$, if the medium is kept neutral by adding alkali.

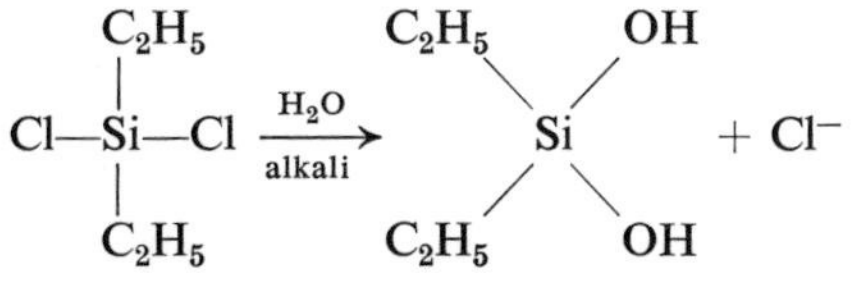

$$Cl-\underset{\underset{C_2H_5}{|}}{\overset{\overset{C_2H_5}{|}}{Si}}-Cl \xrightarrow[alkali]{H_2O} \underset{\underset{C_2H_5}{\diagup \quad \diagdown}}{\overset{C_2H_5 \diagdown \quad \diagup OH}{Si}} + Cl^- \qquad (Exp. 4.24)$$

diethylsilanediol

Tailor-made siloxanes of predictable molecular mass can be synthesized by the hydrolysis of a mixture of mono- and dichloro-silanes in known ratios. For example, a polymer of fairly uniform molecular mass can be obtained by hydrolyzing a mixture of five parts dimethyldichlorosilane and two parts trimethylchlorosilane (Exp. 4.25).

FIGURE 4.7 *Polymeric silicate ions of the chain type in* (a) *pyroxenes and* (b) *amphibole. Polymeric structure of the layer type in* (c) *vermiculite, a complex* Mg, Fe, Al *silicate.* (*Redrawn from Wells, Structural Inorganic Chemistry, Oxford Univ. Press, London and New York* (1962), *3rd ed., pp. 799 and 806; by permission.*)

$$2\ CH_3{-}\underset{\underset{CH_3}{|}}{\overset{\overset{CH_3}{|}}{Si}}{-}Cl + 5\ \underset{\underset{CH_3}{\diagup}\ \ \underset{Cl}{\diagdown}}{\overset{\overset{CH_3}{\diagdown}\ \ \overset{Cl}{\diagup}}{Si}} \longrightarrow (CH_3)_3SiOH + (CH_3)_2Si(OH)_2 \xrightarrow{\ -H_2O\ }$$

$$CH_3{-}\underset{\underset{CH_3}{|}}{\overset{\overset{CH_3}{|}}{Si}}{-}O{-}\Bigg[\underset{\underset{CH_3}{|}}{\overset{\overset{CH_3}{|}}{Si}}{-}O\Bigg]_5\underset{\underset{CH_3}{|}}{\overset{\overset{CH_3}{|}}{Si}}{-}CH_3 \quad (Exp.\ 4.25)$$

a "silicone oil"

The resulting polymer has no C—C bonds and is remarkably stable at high temperatures (400°–500°). These silicone oils have been used as heat transfer liquids since they are heat stable.

Anhydride Formation

An acid anhydride (Table 4.1) is an oxygen-containing compound that reacts with water to form only acids. The oxides in all of the following examples (Eqs. 4.26 to 4.31) react readily with water to form the corresponding acids.

$$\underset{S}{\overset{O\diagdown\ \diagup O}{}} + HOH \longrightarrow \underset{\underset{O}{\parallel}}{\overset{HO\diagdown\ \diagup OH}{S}} \qquad (Eq.\ 4.26)$$

$$\underset{\underset{O}{\parallel}}{\overset{O\diagdown\ \diagup O}{S}} + HOH \longrightarrow \underset{HO\diagup\ \diagdown O}{\overset{HO\diagdown\ \diagup O}{S}} \qquad (Eq.\ 4.27)$$

$$P_4O_6 + 6\ HOH \longrightarrow 4\ \underset{H\diagup\ \diagdown OH}{\overset{HO\diagdown\ \diagup O}{P}} \qquad (Eq.\ 4.28)$$

$$\underset{O\diagup\ \ \ \diagdown O}{\overset{O\diagdown\ \ \ \diagup O}{N{-}O{-}N}} + HOH \longrightarrow 2\ \underset{O}{\overset{O\diagdown\ \diagup}{HO{-}N}} \qquad (Eq.\ 4.29)$$

$$\underset{\overset{O}{\parallel}}{CH_3{-}C}{-}O{-}\underset{\overset{O}{\parallel}}{C}{-}CH_3 + HOH \longrightarrow 2\ CH_3{-}\underset{\overset{O}{\parallel}}{C}{-}OH \qquad (Eq.\ 4.30)$$

$$\underset{CH_2{-}C{=}O}{\overset{CH_2{-}C{=}O}{\diagdown O \diagup}} + HOH \longrightarrow HO{-}\underset{\overset{O}{\parallel}}{C}{-}CH_2CH_2{-}\underset{\overset{O}{\parallel}}{C}{-}OH \qquad (Eq.\ 4.31)$$

Table 4.1 ACID ANHYDRIDES

Acid anhydride	mp (°C)	bp (°C)	Solubility in H_2O
CO_2	−78.5	—	0.145 g/100 g at 25°
$(SiO_2)_n$	1610 (quartz)	2230	insoluble
SO_2	−75	−10	22.8 g/100 g at 0°
SO_3	17	45	dec to $(HO)_2SO_2$
P_4O_6	24	173	dec to $(HO)_2PH(O)$
P_4O_{10}	563	—	dec to $(HO)_3PO$
N_2O_5	30	47	dec to $HONO_2$
$(CH_3CO)_2O$	−73	140	13.6 g/100 g; dec slowly in cold
$\begin{array}{c} CH_2\text{—}C\text{=}O \\ \quad\quad\searrow \\ \quad\quad\quad O \\ \quad\quad\nearrow \\ CH_2\text{—}C\text{=}O \end{array}$	120	261	very slightly soluble

Each oxide, then, is the anhydride of the acid shown as product. The last two anhydrides (Eqs. 4.30 and 4.31) carry C—C bonds, but other than this formal difference, there is no need to set those two reactants apart from the oxides of the nonmetals of the upper right-hand side of the periodic table.

Covalent oxyhalides (Table 4.2) are closely related in properties to acid anhydrides. By definition they may be called "mixed anhydrides" since they form two different acids upon hydrolysis (Eqs. 4.32 to 4.39), one of which is the corresponding hydrohalogen acid.

The covalent oxyhalides are insidious substances whose vapors attack metallic laboratory equipment and the respiratory tract in the body with about equal facility. Carbon oxychloride (phosgene) is a war gas, sulfur(IV) oxychloride vapors give the sensation of a film over the eyes, and phosphorus(V) oxychloride persists in the lining of the nose for several hours after exposure. Obviously, care must be taken in handling these compounds.

Probably much of the deleterious effect of the covalent halides on the lungs is due to the rapid release of HCl by reaction with water vapor (Eqs. 4.32 to 4.39).

Table 4.2 PROPERTIES OF OXYCHLORIDES

Group	Formula	mp (°C)	bp (°C)	Density (g/ml)	Color
IV	$COCl_2$	−119	8	1.39	colorless
	$CH_3\text{—}COCl$	−112	52	1.11	colorless
	$C_6H_5\text{—}COCl$	−1	197	1.22	colorless
V	$NOCl$	−65	−6	—	orange-yellow
	NO_2Cl	−145	−16	—	colorless
	$POCl_3$	1	105	1.67	colorless
VI	$SOCl_2$	−105	78	1.67	yellow
	SO_2Cl_2	−54	69	1.66	colorless
	CH_3SO_2Cl	—	160	1.51	colorless
	$C_6H_5SO_2Cl$	14	247 dec	1.38	colorless
	$SeOCl_2$	8	176	2.42	colorless
	CrO_2Cl_2	—	118	1.96	red

Group

IV
$$COCl_2 + HOH \longrightarrow CO(OH)_2 + 2\ HCl \qquad \text{(Eq. 4.32)}$$
$$\qquad\qquad\qquad\quad \longrightarrow CO_2 + H_2O$$
$$CH_3COCl + HOH \longrightarrow CH_3COOH + HCl \qquad \text{(Eq. 4.33)}$$

V
$$NOCl + HOH \longrightarrow HONO + HCl \qquad \text{(Eq. 4.34)}$$
$$POCl_3 + 3\ HOH \longrightarrow PO(OH)_3 + 3\ HCl \qquad \text{(Eq. 4.35)}$$

VI
$$SOCl_2 + 2\ HOH \longrightarrow SO(OH)_2 + 2\ HCl \qquad \text{(Eq. 4.36)}$$
$$\qquad\qquad\qquad\quad \longrightarrow SO_2 + H_2O$$
$$SO_2Cl_2 + 2\ H_2O \longrightarrow SO_2(OH)_2 + 2\ HCl \qquad \text{(Eq. 4.37)}$$
$$CH_3SO_2Cl + HOH \longrightarrow CH_3SO_2OH + HCl \qquad \text{(Eq. 4.38)}$$
$$CrO_2Cl_2 + 2\ HOH \longrightarrow CrO_2(OH)_2 + 2\ HCl \qquad \text{(Eq. 4.39)}$$

The heat evolved in the conversion to the two acids is frequently enough to generate steam from the water. Often this results in spattering as the halide is dropped into water. The vigorous activity of these compounds generally makes a partial hydrolysis impractical, even though recognizable partial hydrolysis products are known. Chlorosulfonic acid and fluorophosphonic acid may be considered partial hydrolysis products of $SOCl_2$ and POF_3 respectively, but—as the following equations demonstrate—they must be synthesized by reactions not involving hydrolysis.

$$SO_3 + HCl \longrightarrow Cl-\overset{\displaystyle O}{\underset{\displaystyle O}{\overset{|}{\underset{|}{S}}}}-OH \qquad \text{(Eq. 4.40)}$$

bp 152°C, chlorosulfonic
acid

$$HOPO_2 + HF \longrightarrow F-\overset{\displaystyle OH}{\underset{\displaystyle O}{\overset{|}{\underset{|}{P}}}}-OH \qquad \text{(Eq. 4.41)}$$

fluorophosphonic
acid

The reactions of acid anhydrides or oxyhalides with water are not commonly useful, since the products are generally cheaper than the starting compounds. Nevertheless, the chemist must be aware of these vigorous hydrolytic reactions in order to prevent loss of acid anhydride or oxyhalide in undesired side reactions. In using these compounds, strictly dry apparatus must therefore be employed.

The intramolecular atrophy of the elements of water in phosphorus, nitrogen, and sulfur acids (the reverse of the hydrolysis of an anhydride) has already been discussed on pages 53 to 58. The loss of water at elevated temperature to give anhydrides, of course, would be the completion of a use-less synthetic cycle which commonly starts with a simple combustion of the element. It would be uneconomical to remove water from a compound that had just been made by the addition of water. As an example, phosphorus may be burned in an excess of air to form phosphoric anhydride, P_4O_{10} (Exp. 4.42).

$$P_4 + 5\,O_2 \longrightarrow P_4O_{10} \xrightarrow{\text{H}_2\text{O}} (HO)_3PO \xrightarrow{\text{H}_2\text{O}} HOPO_2 \quad (\text{Exp. 4.42})$$

This may be hydrolyzed to orthophosphoric acid (Exp. 4.42) and dehydrated to metaphosphoric acid (Fig. 4.1; Eq. 4.4), but the return to P_4O_{10} from either phosphoric acid would be a completion of a useless cycle.

Ester Formation

The formal relationships among compounds containing common linkages are worth more than a passing glance. One of the principal values is in guiding the chemist to the realm of imaginative synthesis. We have shown that there is a formal relationship among water, alcohols, and ethers through the loss of the elements of water (p. 37), and we have looked at some diff-erences between C—OH and Si—OH linkages (pp. 59–66). Acid anhydrides bear an analogous relationship among the series water, acid, and anhydride. Intramolecular loss of H_2O between alcohols and acids leads in a formal way to esters (Fig. 4.8, p. 70), and we have described ways of getting to esters in the laboratory (p. 31).

The detailed instructions and recipes for arriving at particular compounds among these series (Fig. 4.8) vary widely since the boiling points, solubilities, molecular masses, and other properties vary widely. In a manner of speaking, we have omitted these details about the individual trees to take an overall look at the forest.

Generalizations Concerning Condensations of OH Groups

When a central atom in $G(OH)_n$ carries one or more OH groups, the pathway of condensation leads in different directions, depending on n:

1. When $n = 1$, condensation by dehydration leads to a dimer. For example, alcohols can be condensed to ethers (Eq. 2.46, Exp. 4.23); acids condense to anhydrides (p. 66), and acids condense with alcohols to form esters (p. 31). The relationships are summarized in Fig. 4.8.

2. When $n = 2$, condensation by dehydration may lead to monomers, but also to cyclic or linear polymers.

Elements in the second row in the periodic table form multiple bonds to a much greater extent than elements in lower rows, thus leading to monomers. In the context of this chapter, hydroxy groups attached to elements in the second row will have a greater tendency to condense with loss of a molecule of water intramolecularly (Exp. 4.20) than hydroxy groups attached to

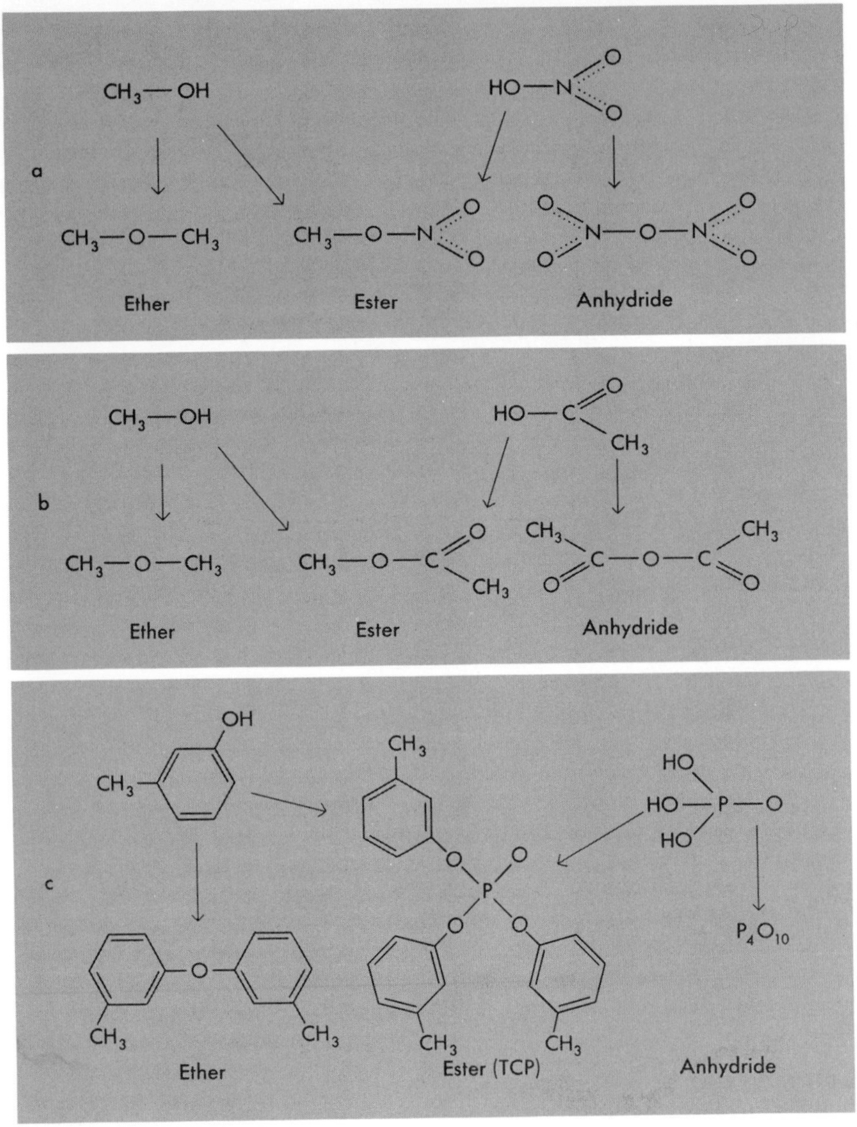

FIGURE 4.8 *Atrophy in hydroxy compounds: (a) alcohol → ether; (b) acid → anhydride; (c) alcohol + acid → ester.*

elements in the third or lower rows (Exp. 4.19). In terms of structure, double-bond formation with oxygen in the second row elements occurs in preference to single-bond formation because the central atom is small and π overlap gives stronger bonds.

$$M\text{—OH} \longrightarrow M\text{=-O} + H_2O$$
$$\diagdown$$
$$OH$$

For example, the bond strength of the carbon-oxygen bond (double) in carbon dioxide is 192 kcal/mole, while the carbon-oxygen bond strength in methanol (single) is 90 kcal/mole, less than half as great. The larger silicon atom apparently cannot form a strong π bond (p_π-d_π) with oxygen; the silicon-oxygen multiple bond is rare, if not unknown.

Nitrogen acids lose water only by intramolecular condensation and multiple bond formation with oxygen (N_2O_5). Sulfur acids form sulfates and pyrosulfates but also a cyclic trimeric anhydride (SO_3)$_3$ by intermolecular condensation. Silicones (Exp. 4.25) result from intermolecular condensation.

3. When $n > 2$, three-dimensional polymers are possible as well as the condensation types of points 1 and 2 above.

Phosphoric acid condenses both intramolecularly to form orthophosphoric acid and intermolecularly to form metaphosphoric acid (cyclic trimer), pyrophosphoric acid, and polyphosphoric acids (Fig. 4.2).

When three OH groups are attached to a central atom (silicon, for example) a 3-dimensional network polymer is possible (Exp. 4.21 and Fig. 4.6).

Silicon and aluminum readily form polymeric silicates and aluminates (Fig. 4.7). The latter examples are manifestations of intermolecular atrophy.

Elements in the third row in the periodic table form polyacids readily, and the tendency increases from right to left in this row.

New Directions

Can we use the formal relationships we have established to study old diseases in new molecules? Since electronic structures govern some properties, can we make use of the chemistry of OH in groups isoelectronic with OH, such as NH_2, or an analogous group from the same period as OH, such as SH?

$$\begin{array}{ccc} & \overset{\displaystyle H}{\underset{\displaystyle \cdots}{\cdot N}} : H & \\ \cdot \overset{\cdots}{\underset{\cdots}{O}} : H & & \cdot \overset{\cdots}{\underset{\cdots}{S}} : H \end{array}$$

The answer to these questions is worth a chapter by itself (Chapter 5).

Exercise 4.1. Predict the effect of water on each indicated substance by writing a suitable equation:

a. C_6H_5—C—O—C—C_6H_5 f.

         ∥   ∥
         O   O

b. As_2O_5 g. N_2O_3
c. $H_2S_2O_7$ h. CH_3—CH_2—COCl
d. $CHCl_3$ i. CaO
e. $SiHCl_3$ j. SO_2

Exercise 4.2. With the use of reference books, write formulas for all forms of the acids in highest oxidation state of all elements in

     a.   Group Va
     b.   Group VIa
     c.   Group VIIa

Do you find a pattern in this set of compounds with respect to occurrence of *ortho* and *meta* forms of these acids within these groups?

5

The Nitrogen System

of Compounds

Isosteres

The element to the left of oxygen in the periodic table forms a hydride (NH_3) with the same number of electrons (10) as water (H_2O). Molecules with the same number of electrons are said to be *isoelectronic*. These molecules, and analogous groups derived from them, are called *isosteres*.[1] In Table 5.1, water and ammonia are isosteres; among other isosteres are H_3O^+ and NH_4^+, OH^- and NH_2^-, —OH and —NH_2 groups, and —O— and —NH— groups. Isosteres have many properties in common. It will be the purpose of this chapter to examine the usefulness of the concept of isosteres.

Ammonia and Metals

Ammonia is a weak base of strong odor and is gaseous at room temperature. A comparison of the properties of water and ammonia is depicted in Table 5.2.

[1] The original term *isoster*, first used by Irving Langmuir, *J. Am. Chem. Soc.*, **41**, 868, 1543 (1919) was restricted to molecules (or groups) of the same number of *atoms* and the same number of *electrons*, such as CO and N_2, CO_2 and N_2O, N_3 and NCO^-, etc. *Isostere* is used here to mean molecules or groups with the same number of electrons.

Table 5.1 ISOSTERES

Oxygen system		Nitrogen System	
H:Ö:H	water	H:N̈:H H	ammonia
H Ö:H⁺ H	hydronium ion	H H:N̈:H⁺ H	ammonium ion
:Ö:H⁻	hydroxide ion	:N̈:H⁻ H	amide ion
—OH or · Ö:H	hydroxyl group	—NH₂ or · N̈:H H	amino group
—O— or · Ö ·	ether function	—NH or · N̈ · H	imide group

By reference to the chemical reactions of water (page 22 ff.) we find some useful parallels in the nitrogen isostere, ammonia. Sodium will displace one hydrogen from water and also from ammonia (Eqs. 5.1 and 5.2), and at high temperature all hydrogens may be displaced from either by an active metal (Eqs. 5.4 and 5.5). These reactions of water and ammonia, then, are analogous in character.

$$Na_{(s)} + H_2O_{(l)} \xrightarrow{25°} Na^+OH^-_{(aq)} + \tfrac{1}{2} H_{2(g)} \qquad \text{(Eq. 5.1)}$$

$$Na_{(s)} + NH_{3(l)} \xrightarrow{Fe^{3+}} Na^+NH^-_{2(s)} + \tfrac{1}{2} H_{2(g)} \qquad \text{(Eq. 5.2)}$$

[As a result of a difference in rates of the two reactions, sodium simply dissolves in liquid ammonia, in the absence of a catalyst, to give a deep blue color, and is recovered unchanged as the ammonia boils away. In the presence of an iron(III) catalyst, hydrogen is displaced (Eq. 5.2).]

Sodium amide ($Na^+NH_2^-$) is best prepared in quantity by passing ammonia gas over sodium at a temperature high enough to keep both sodium and sodium amide molten (Eq. 5.3).

$$Na_{(l)} + NH_{3(g)} \xrightarrow{210°} Na^+NH^-_{2(l)} + \tfrac{1}{2} H_{2(g)} \qquad \text{(Eq. 5.3)}$$

Table 5.2 PROPERTIES OF WATER AND AMMONIA

	Water	Ammonia
Formula mass	18	17
mp(°C)	0	−78
bp(°C)	100	−33
Density at bp (g/ml)	0.958	0.683
Dielectric Constant, ε	80.37 at 20°	22.4 at −33°
Dipole Moment (μ)	1.84D	1.47D
Sodium Compound	NaOH	NaNH₂
mp(°C) of sodium compound	318	210

The salt (Eq. 5.5) formed from the displacement of all the hydrogen from ammonia is called a nitride (compare oxide). Thus, magnesium will react at elevated temperature with gaseous ammonia to produce magnesium nitride.

$$3 \, Fe_{(s)} + 4 \, H_2O_{(g)} \xrightarrow{1000°} Fe_3O_{4(s)} + 4 \, H_{2(g)} \tag{Eq. 5.4}$$

$$3 \, Mg_{(s)} + 2 \, NH_{3(g)} \xrightarrow{\Delta} (Mg^{++})_3(N^{3-})_{2(s)} + 3 \, H_{2(g)} \tag{Eq. 5.5}$$

Ammonia as Acid and as Base

Parallel reactions of water and ammonia as acids and as bases may be written for these two isosteres. Toward HCl, for example, ammonia and water both act as bases and are converted to the corresponding isosteric conjugate acids, NH_4^+ and H_3O^+ (Eqs. 5.6 and 5.7).

$$\underset{base_1}{H_2O_{(l)}} + \underset{acid_2}{HCl_{(g)}} \rightleftharpoons \underset{acid_1}{H_3O^+_{(aq)}} + \underset{base_2}{Cl^-_{(aq)}} \tag{Eq. 5.6}$$

$$NH_{3(aq)} + HCl_{(g)} \rightleftharpoons NH_4^+_{(aq)} + Cl^-_{(aq)} \tag{Eq. 5.7}$$

In the first of these reactions (Eq. 5.6) water is a weak base but HCl is a strong enough acid to protonate it anyhow. Ammonia is a stronger base than water so the equilibrium in Eq. 5.7 lies farther to the right than the equilibrium of Eq. 5.6. As bases, then, NH_3 is stronger than H_2O. The conjugate relationship also holds: the conjugate acids will have strengths in reverse order—that is, H_3O^+ is a stronger acid than NH_4^+.

The acidic character of ammonia in the Brönsted-Lowry sense is best illustrated in parallel with water by reaction with the same base, $^-OC_2H_5$, in ethyl alcohol as solvent.

$$\underset{acid_1}{H_2O} + \underset{base_2}{OC_2H_5^-} \rightleftharpoons \underset{acid_2}{C_2H_5OH} + \underset{base_1}{OH^-} \tag{Eq. 5.8}$$

$$\underset{acid_1}{NH_3} + \underset{base_2}{OC_2H_5^-} \rightleftharpoons \underset{acid_2}{C_2H_5OH} + \underset{base_1}{NH_2^-} \tag{Eq. 5.9}$$

The reaction of sodium ethoxide with water is very rapid and essentially complete so that the equilibrium in Eq. 5.8 lies overwhelmingly to the right. On the other hand, ammonia is a weaker acid than water so that the same base, $OC_2H_5^-$, reacts with NH_3 to a lesser extent. The new base (NH_2^-) and new acid (C_2H_5OH) are more compatible with reactants than $acid_2$ and $base_1$ in Eq. 5.8. The conjugate relationship also holds in this case as well. The amide ion (NH_2^-) is a stronger base than hydroxide ion (OH^-). The equilibrium of Eq. 5.8 lies farther to the right than that of Eq. 5.9.

In any acid-base reaction, then, the equilibrium always lies on the side of the weaker of two acids and thus (necessarily) on the side of the weaker of the two bases. In Eq. 5.8, for example, water (acid$_1$) is a stronger acid than ethyl alcohol (acid$_2$) and $^-OC_2H_5$ (base$_2$) is a stronger base than OH$^-$ (base$_1$).

Ammonolysis

Hydrolysis and alcoholysis reactions of the covalent halide, PCl$_3$, were considered in Chapter 2. The hydrolysis of anhydrides and oxyhalides has been delineated in Chapter 4. We can profitably consider the ammonolysis (reaction with ammonia) of these same groups of compounds in an analogous fashion. E. C. Franklin, an American chemist, was the first to emphasize the efficacy of the formal relationship between isosteres in the oxygen and nitrogen *systems* of compounds. He was the first to suggest that studying a *system* of compounds as a whole group simplified the correlation of the chemistry markedly. The detailed properties of nitrogen and oxygen analogs may not bear close resemblances, but as a means of predicting possible paths of reactions and predicting the possible existence of new substances in a second system of compounds, the idea is valuable.

On a formal basis, then, we could write a series of ammonolysis reactions by looking at the corresponding hydrolysis and alcoholysis products (Exps. 5.10, 5.11) of the carbon oxychloride called phosgene. The ammonolysis of phosgene gives the corresponding compound in the nitrogen system (Exp. 5.12). It is called urea, a product of metabolism in animals.

$$\underset{\text{phosgene}}{\overset{\displaystyle Cl}{\underset{\displaystyle Cl}{\diagup\!\!\!C{=}O\diagdown}}} + 2\,HOH \longrightarrow \underset{\text{carbonic acid}}{\overset{\displaystyle OH}{\underset{\displaystyle OH}{\diagup\!\!\!C{=}O\diagdown}}} + 2\,HCl \qquad \text{(Exp. 5.10)}$$

$$\overset{\displaystyle Cl}{\underset{\displaystyle Cl}{\diagup\!\!\!C{=}O\diagdown}} + 2\,C_2H_5OH \longrightarrow \underset{\text{ethyl carbonate}}{\overset{\displaystyle OC_2H_5}{\underset{\displaystyle OC_2H_5}{\diagup\!\!\!C{=}O\diagdown}}} + 2\,HCl \qquad \text{(Exp. 5.11)}$$

$$\overset{\displaystyle Cl}{\underset{\displaystyle Cl}{\diagup\!\!\!C{=}O\diagdown}} + 2\,NH_3 \longrightarrow \underset{\text{urea}}{\overset{\displaystyle NH_2}{\underset{\displaystyle NH_2}{\diagup\!\!\!C{=}O\diagdown}}} + 2\,HCl \qquad \text{(Exp. 5.12)}$$

It is to be noted that HCl will not remain free in any of the three reactions. It will react with excess of the solvent to give H$_3$O$^+$Cl$^-$, C$_2$H$_5$OH$_2$$^+Cl^-$, and NH$_4$$^+Cl^-$, respectively. This secondary reaction is omitted here for simplification, although to do so gives an incomplete picture.

Simply by replacing the halogen with an NH$_2$ group, the ammonolysis products can be written for other oxyhalides (Exps. 5.13–5.15), anhydrides (Exp. 5.16), and covalent halides (Exp. 5.17).

$$SO_2Cl_2 + NH_3 \longrightarrow SO_2(NH_2)_2 + 2\,HCl \qquad \text{(Exp. 5.13)}$$

$$NOCl + NH_3 \longrightarrow NO(NH_2) + HCl$$
$$\quad\quad\quad\quad\quad\quad\quad\Big|_{\longrightarrow N_2 + H_2O} \qquad \text{(Exp. 5.14)}$$

$$CH_3\!-\!\underset{\underset{O}{\|}}{C}\!-\!Cl + 2\,NH_3 \longrightarrow CH_3\!-\!\underset{\underset{O}{\|}}{C}\!-\!NH_2 + NH_4{}^+Cl^- \qquad \text{(Exp. 5.15)}$$

$$(CH_3\!-\!\overset{\overset{O}{\|}}{C})_2\!-\!O + 2\,NH_3 \longrightarrow CH_3\!-\!\underset{\underset{O}{\|}}{C}\!-\!NH_2 + CH_3\!-\!\underset{\underset{O}{\|}}{C}\!-\!O^-NH_4{}^+$$
$$\text{(Exp. 5.16)}$$

$$PCl_3 + 3\,NH_3 \longrightarrow P(NH_2)_3 + 3\,HCl \qquad \text{(Exp. 5.17)}$$

These expressions do not tell the full story, however. In Exp. 5.14, for example, the product ($ON\!-\!NH_2$) cannot in fact be isolated; if it is formed at all, decomposition occurs to give nitrogen and water as the final products. Franklin's system, although a powerful aid in suggesting possible reactions, must therefore be used with caution: it does not predict properties of expected products.

The analogous behavior of oxyhalides and acid anhydrides is exemplified in Exps. 5.15 and 5.16. The reaction in Exp. 5.15 is a displacement of the halogen by an NH_2 group. The second ammonia molecule and the extra hydrogen give a salt of the hydrohalogen acid ammonium chloride, $NH_4{}^+Cl^-$. The reaction in Exp. 5.16 is a displacement of the acetate group by an NH_2 group. The second ammonia molecule and the extra hydrogen give a salt of acetic acid, ammonium acetate ($CH_3\!-\!COO^-NH_4{}^+$). The two reactions (Exps. 5.15 and 5.16) are completely analogous and are about equally vigorous at the bench.

The product $P(NH_2)_3$ in Exp. 5.17 is the parent compound for a series of derivatives of what may be called the phosphorus-nitrogen system of compounds (page 80).

Exercise 5.1 Write possible ammonolysis products for the oxyhalides $SOCl_2$, $SbOCl$, and $SeOCl_2$.

Exercise 5.2. Write possible ammonolysis products for the following covalent halides: $SbCl_3$, BCl_3, and $TiCl_4$.

Partial Hydrolysis, Alcoholysis, and Ammonolysis Reactions

With covalent halides or oxyhalides in which three halogen atoms are attached to the central atom, it is possible (on paper at least) to write mixed solvolysis reactions in which water, alcohol, and ammonia are all involved (or two of the three, in case only two halogen atoms are available). The possibility of mixed alcoholysis-hydrolysis reactions at the bench may be feasible (below), and the possibility of introducing ammonia as another solvolytic agent further increases the number of products.

We shall consider the mixed solvolysis of $POCl_3$ as an example (below). Hydrolysis of $POCl_3$ may be thought of for our purposes as proceeding stepwise as follows:

$$
O-P\begin{smallmatrix} Cl \\ \diagup \\ -Cl \\ \diagdown \\ Cl \end{smallmatrix} \xrightarrow{H_2O} O-P\begin{smallmatrix} OH \\ \diagup \\ -Cl \\ \diagdown \\ Cl \end{smallmatrix} \longrightarrow O-P\begin{smallmatrix} OH \\ \diagup \\ -OH \\ \diagdown \\ Cl \end{smallmatrix} \longrightarrow O-P\begin{smallmatrix} OH \\ \diagup \\ -OH \\ \diagdown \\ OH \end{smallmatrix} \quad \text{(Exp. 5.18)}
$$

(a)

Correspondingly intermediate alcoholysis and ammonolysis products of $POCl_3$ are given in Exps. 5.19 and 5.20, respectively.

$$
O-P\begin{smallmatrix} Cl \\ \diagup \\ -Cl \\ \diagdown \\ Cl \end{smallmatrix} \xrightarrow{C_2H_5OH} O-P\begin{smallmatrix} OC_2H_5 \\ \diagup \\ -Cl \\ \diagdown \\ Cl \end{smallmatrix} \longrightarrow
$$

(a)

$$
O-P\begin{smallmatrix} OC_2H_5 \\ \diagup \\ -OC_2H_5 \\ \diagdown \\ Cl \end{smallmatrix} \longrightarrow O-P\begin{smallmatrix} OC_2H_5 \\ \diagup \\ -OC_2H_5 \\ \diagdown \\ OC_2H_5 \end{smallmatrix} \quad \text{(Exp. 5.19)}
$$

$$
O-P\begin{smallmatrix} Cl \\ \diagup \\ -Cl \\ \diagdown \\ Cl \end{smallmatrix} \xrightarrow{NH_3} O-P\begin{smallmatrix} NH_2 \\ | \\ -Cl \\ \diagdown \\ Cl \end{smallmatrix} \longrightarrow O-P\begin{smallmatrix} NH_2 \\ \diagup \\ -NH_2 \\ \diagdown \\ Cl \end{smallmatrix} \longrightarrow O-P\begin{smallmatrix} NH_2 \\ \diagup \\ -NH_2 \\ \diagdown \\ NH_2 \end{smallmatrix}
$$

(a)   (Exp. 5.20)

Mixed Solvolysis Reactions

It will be evident that the intermediates, 18a, 19a, and 20a could on the face of it be used to react with either of the two remaining solvolytic reagents alcohol and ammonia, to give mixed solvolysis products. For example, if the partially hydrolyzed product (18a) is taken as starting compound, then alcoholysis (with ethanol) followed by ammonolysis should give compound 21b.

$$
O-P\begin{smallmatrix} OH \\ \diagup \\ -Cl \\ \diagdown \\ Cl \end{smallmatrix} \xrightarrow{C_2H_5OH} O-P\begin{smallmatrix} OH \\ \diagup \\ -OC_2H_5 \\ \diagdown \\ Cl \end{smallmatrix} \xrightarrow{NH_3} O-P\begin{smallmatrix} OH \\ \diagup \\ -OC_2H_5 \\ \diagdown \\ NH_2 \end{smallmatrix} \quad \text{(Exp. 5.21)}
$$

(18a)   (21a)   (21b)

As might be anticipated, experimental difficulties may get in the way of carrying out all conceivable combinations of these three solvolysis reactions.

With three easily displaced halogens, it may not be possible to prevent two halogens in one molecule from being displaced while none in a second molecule react, even with a careful measurement and addition of one mole of the solvolytic reagent. A few reactions have been performed successfully involving two of the three solvolyses. Examples of successful reactions are shown in Exp. 5.22.

The C_6H_5 group increases the molecular mass of the first intermediate (22a), cuts the number of available halogens by one-third, and changes the molecular torso which faces the new reacting ammonia molecule. The reactivity of the remaining halogens in the intermediate is reduced to a controllable vigor by the changes in orientation, reduction in probability of encounter of halogen with reagent, and sheer bulk. Whether increase in molecular mass is a contributing factor to reduced activity, independent of bulk and orientation, is not easy to determine.

$$
POCl_3 + HO\!-\!C_6H_5 \longrightarrow O\!-\!\underset{\underset{Cl}{|}}{\overset{\overset{OC_6H_5}{|}}{P}}\!-\!Cl \longrightarrow O\!-\!\underset{\underset{Cl}{|}}{\overset{\overset{OC_6H_5}{|}}{P}}\!-\!OC_6H_5 \quad \text{(Exp. 5.22)}
$$

(a)

$$
\overset{NH_3}{\Big\downarrow} \qquad\qquad \overset{NH_3}{\Big\downarrow}
$$

$$
O\!-\!\underset{\underset{NH_2}{}}{\overset{\overset{OC_6H_5}{|}}{P}}\!-\!NH_2 \qquad O\!-\!\underset{\underset{NH_2}{}}{\overset{\overset{OC_6H_5}{|}}{P}}\!-\!OC_6H_5
$$

When only two halogens are involved as functional groups, clear-cut synthetic products are somewhat easier to isolate. Phosgene, for example, can be treated with ethanol, and the partially esterified product (Exp. 5.23) can be subjected to ammonolysis successfully (Exp. 5.24).

$$
\underset{\underset{Cl}{\diagdown}}{\overset{\overset{Cl}{\diagup}}{C}}\!=\!O + C_2H_5OH \longrightarrow \underset{\underset{OC_2H_5}{\diagdown}}{\overset{\overset{Cl}{\diagup}}{C}}\!=\!O + HCl \qquad \text{(Exp. 5.23)}
$$

phosgene   ethyl chlorocarbonate

(a)

$$
\underset{\underset{OC_2H_5}{\diagdown}}{\overset{\overset{Cl}{\diagup}}{C}}\!=\!O + NH_3 \longrightarrow \underset{\underset{OC_2H_5}{\diagdown}}{\overset{\overset{NH_2}{\diagup}}{C}}\!=\!O + HCl \qquad \text{(Exp. 5.24)}
$$

ethyl carbamate

The corresponding hydrolysis product of the half ester (23a) is unstable, however, and only water, HCl (not shown), and CO_2 are obtained (Exp. 5.25) in the reaction of ethyl chlorocarbonate with water.

$$
\begin{array}{c}
\text{Cl} \\
\diagup \\
\text{C}\!=\!\text{O} \\
\diagdown \\
\text{OC}_2\text{H}_5
\end{array}
\; + \text{H}_2\text{O} \longrightarrow
\left[
\begin{array}{c}
\text{OH} \\
\diagup \\
\text{C}\!=\!\text{O} \\
\diagdown \\
\text{OC}_2\text{H}_5
\end{array}
\right]
\longrightarrow \text{C}_2\text{H}_5\text{OH} + \text{CO}_2 \quad (\text{Exp. 5.25})
$$

A new aspect of these reactions is shown in Exp. 5.26.

$$
\begin{array}{c}
\text{NH}_2 \\
\diagup \\
\text{C}\!=\!\text{O} \\
\diagdown \\
\text{OC}_2\text{H}_5 \\
\text{ethyl carbamate}
\end{array}
\xrightarrow{\text{NH}_3}
\begin{array}{c}
\text{NH}_2 \\
\diagup \\
\text{C}\!=\!\text{O} \\
\diagdown \\
\text{NH}_2 \\
\text{urea}
\end{array}
\xleftarrow{\text{NH}_3}
\begin{array}{c}
\text{OC}_2\text{H}_5 \\
\diagup \\
\text{C}\!=\!\text{O} \\
\diagdown \\
\text{OC}_2\text{H}_5 \\
\text{ethyl carbonate}
\end{array}
\quad (\text{Exp. 5.26})
$$

Water, ammonia, and alcohol all react readily with oxyhalides such as phosgene to displace halogen (Exps. 5.10–5.12). But an OC_2H_5 group is itself displaced by ammonia in either ethyl carbamate or ethyl carbonate (Exp. 5.26). Ammonia, then, will commonly displace halogen from a covalent halide or oxyhalide, an ethoxy (OC_2H_5) group from an ester, or an oxygen from an anhydride to substitute an NH_2 group on the central atom. This opens new synthetic paths to what may be called an *ammono system* of compounds (Table 5.3).

Exercise 5.3. Write equations for the reaction of the following anhydride with each reagent indicated:

$$
\begin{array}{c}
\text{CH}_2\!-\!\text{C}\!=\!\text{O} \\
| \qquad\qquad \diagdown \\
\qquad\qquad\qquad \text{O} \\
| \qquad\qquad \diagup \\
\text{CH}_2\!-\!\text{C}\!=\!\text{O}
\end{array}
$$

a. water

b. ammonia

c. ethyl alcohol

Exercise 5.4. Write an equation for the reaction between ammonia and

$$\text{HOOC}\!-\!\text{CH}_2\!-\!\text{CH}_2\!-\!\text{COOC}_2\text{H}_5$$

Relative Reactivity of Oxyhalides

The relative reactivity of the oxyhalides can be correlated with the molecular mass of the compound although why the correlation exists is not clear (compare pp. 77–79). All of the oxyhalides of low molecular mass (below 150, for example) are extremely reactive. In compounds with carbon as the central atom carrying the oxygen and chlorine, there is a distinct difference in the reactivity of substrates of quite different molecular mass—for example, CH_3COCl and C_6H_5COCl. Hydrolysis and ammonolysis of CH_3COCl are rather violent. The heat evolved when CH_3COCl is dropped into water at room temperature may be enough to generate steam in a small local spot and manifest itself in a hissing sound.

$$CH_3-\overset{\displaystyle O}{\underset{\displaystyle Cl}{C}} + HOH \longrightarrow CH_3-\overset{\displaystyle O}{\underset{\displaystyle OH}{C}} + HCl \qquad (Exp.\ 5.27)$$
acetic acid

$$CH_3-\overset{\displaystyle O}{\underset{\displaystyle Cl}{C}} + NH_3 \longrightarrow CH_3-\overset{\displaystyle O}{\underset{\displaystyle NH_2}{C}} + HCl \qquad (Exp.\ 5.28)$$
acetamide

The oxychlorides of higher formula mass may need to be helped along in hydrolysis and ammonolysis reactions by the introduction of base into the reaction mixture. This is the case, for example, with benzoyl chloride (Eq. 5.29) or benzenesulfonyl chloride (Eq. 5.30). These both require rather prolonged shaking in a test tube with a base to get appreciable reaction with water or ammonia. Both oxychlorides are completely insoluble in water and hence reaction only takes place at the interface. Shaking changes the surface continuously and allows the reaction to occur, although slowly.

$$C_6H_5COCl + 2\ OH^- \longrightarrow C_6H_5COO^- + Cl^- + H_2O \qquad (Eq.\ 5.29)$$
benzoyl   benzoate
chloride   ion

$$C_6H_5SO_2Cl + NH_3 + 2\ OH^- \longrightarrow C_6H_5-SO_2NH^- + Cl^- + H_2O$$
benzene-   benzene-
sulfonyl chloride   sulfonamide ion

$$(Eq.\ 5.30)$$

The Phosphorus-Nitrogen System of Compounds

In the terms of Franklin, the series of phosphorus acids that have been discussed (pages 53–58) may be called a phosphorus-oxygen system of compounds. The hydrolysis products of phosphorus oxychloride (Exp. 5.18) likewise are members of the P–O system.

Guided by the pattern of dehydration products that we wrote for the parent acid of the phosphorus-oxygen system, $P(OH)_5$, we could assume the possibility of a corresponding parent compound in the phosphorus-nitrogen system, $P(NH_2)_5$. In the P–O system, the parent compound was unknown but we wrote several dehydration products that have been identified (Fig. 4.2). By analogy, we should not be surprised if some of the ammonophosphoric acids that we can write on paper have not been identified at the bench. Indeed, the parent compound, $P(NH_2)_5$, is unknown in the P–N system.

Comparison with the P–O system suggests that the parent compound might suffer deammonation (loss of NH_3) analogous to the loss of H_2O in the P–O system. The results of such deammonations are given in Table 5.3.

Table 5.3 AMMONOPHOSPHORIC ACIDS

The last four (c–f) of these compounds have been prepared and reported in the chemical literature.

Exercise 5.5. Write the phosphorus-nitrogen system ammonolysis products of PCl_3 and the deammonation products that might be expected from them.

Why do you find more about the P–O system of compounds in textbooks than about the P–N system? There may be more than one answer to the general question of why the chemistry of particular systems is not discussed: (1) the compounds may not be important either in the laboratory or commercially; (2) the compounds may be too expensive; (3) the chemistry may have been neglected; (4) the compounds may be difficult to study. Perhaps all of these reasons can be advanced for our unfamiliarity with the P–N system of compounds. In related systems, however, this author is willing to say that the chemistry of the Sb–N, As–N, Si–N, and other systems has simply been neglected for greener pastures. We are suggesting that Franklin's notion of a system of compounds may still be considered one useful way for a beginner in chemistry to get to the edge of research in a particular field to see how a current research problem could be brainstormed. There is room for you here to explore some of the unsolved problems of chemistry of antimony, arsenic, and silicon.

Exercise 5.6. Write ammonolysis and deammonation products for $SbCl_3$, $SbCl_5$, and $AsCl_3$.

Exercise 5.7. Find out how many of the products you write have been described in the literature.

Mixed Systems of Compounds

Our discussion of the P–O and P–N systems of compounds suggests that mixed aquo-ammono systems of acids should be possible. Examples of mixed aquo-ammono acids are known in the sulfur system. A series of aquo-ammonosulfuric acids is presented in Table 5.4.

Replacement (on paper) of a halogen by an OH group in the Group (VI) oxychloride (SO_2Cl_2) gives $ClSO_3H$, chlorosulfonic acid. Chlorosulfonic acid is a strong acid which fumes in moist air and reacts violently with water to give sulfuric acid (which may be said to belong to the S–O system of compounds). Replacement of the halogen in chlorosulfonic acid by the nitrogen isostere of the OH group (NH_2) gives us sulfamic acid, a mixed aquo-ammono acid.

81

Table 5.4 AQUO–AMMONOSULFURIC ACIDS

Sulfamic acid, mp 205°, is interesting to contrast with the common laboratory acids H_2SO_4, HNO_3, and HCl. Sulfamic acid is a white solid, a strong acid that can nevertheless be handled in cardboard cartons. It is easy to crystallize as large flat plates. Unlike the other laboratory acids just mentioned, it is not completely miscible with water. Its solubility is 24 g/100 g H_2O at 25°.

The ammonium salt of sulfamic acid ($NH_4{}^+$ $^-OSO_2NH_2$) is a fire retardant and an excellent weed-killer. It is effective for example, in killing poison-ivy plants.

The next aquo-ammono derivative, sulfamide [$SO_2(NH_2)_2$], is known, and the deammonation product is known in the form of a cyclic trimer, trisulfimide [$(SO_2NH)_3$] (Table 5.4).

Exercise 5.8. Construct a table of aquo-ammonophosphoric acids by suitable processes of dehydration and deammonation on replacement products of $POCl_3$.

Exercise 5.9. What is the sulfur analog of the following substances in the oxygen system?
    a. OH^-
    b. $O^=$
    c. H_2O

Exercise 5.10. What is the nitrogen system isostere of the following compounds in the oxygen system?
    a. H_2O d. CH_3COOH f. $Si(OC_2H_5)_4$
    b. OH^- e. $Si(OH)_4$ g. CH_3COCl
    c. SO_2

Exercise 5.11. Construct a table of aquo-ammono-sulfophosphoric acids from $PSCl_3$ by substitutions of Cl with OH and NH_2, followed by suitable dehydration and deammonation.

Suggested References

Audrieth, L. F., "Nitrogen Derivatives of Phosphorus and Sulfur," *J. Chem. Ed.*, **34**, 545 (1957).

Clapp, L. B., "Some Chemistry of Covalent Compounds with a Single Central Atom," *J. Chem. Ed.*, **30**, 584 (1953).

Emeleus, H. J., "Some Inorganic Polymers," *Proc. Chem. Soc.*, 202 (1959).

Franklin, E. C., *The Nitrogen System of Compounds*, Reinhold Publ. Corp., New York (1935).

Schatz, V. B., "Isosterism and Bio-isosterism as Guides to Structural Variations," Chapter 8 in A. Burger, ed., *Medicinal Chemistry*, John Wiley (Interscience), New York (1960), 2nd ed.

Sowerby, D. B., and Audrieth, L. F., "Inorganic Polymerization Reactions," *J. Chem. Ed.*, **37**, 2 (1960).

6

The Third Dimension

and the OH Group

Many of the figures in this book are drawn with the illusion of three dimensions because the properties in which we are interested often depend on the space-filling character of the groups around the central atom, on symmetry or asymmetry in the molecules, on bond angles, or on bond lengths. In short, the properties depend on the geometry and topology of the molecules. It therefore behooves us to portray the molecular model in three dimensions in terms of current theory.

Dipole Moments

One such aforementioned property, determined by the geometry of the molecule and the distribution of charge within it, is the dipole moment (Fig. 6.1). The dipole moment, μ, is defined as the product of the charge (e) and the distance (r) between the positive and negative charge centers in the system. As an example, the dipole moment of water may be considered to be the resultant of two vectors (Fig. 6.2) formed by the three nuclei at a bond angle of 104.5°. The dipole moment of water is known and the moment of the OH group alone may be calculated from trigonometric relations on the assumption that the resultant vector (dipole moment of water) splits the bond angle in half.

84

$\mu = er$

FIGURE 6.1 *Relationship of the dipole moment μ to charge magnitude and distance of charge separation.*

The unit of negative charge, the electron, has the numerical value of 4.8×10^{-10} esu. Interatomic distances within molecules are of the order of 10^{-8} cm, since the smallest and largest atoms vary only between 0.5×10^{-8} cm and 2.7×10^{-8} cm. Complete separation of charge would result in an ion, so the centers of charge separation where ions are not formed may only be a fraction of the internuclear distances. The unit of dipole moment was selected for this convenience and has therefore been defined as 10^{-10} esu $\times 10^{-8}$ cm $= 10^{-18}$ esu-cm and is called a *Debye unit*. The dipole moment of water as measured in the laboratory is 1.84 Debye units.

In Fig. 6.2, if OA represents the dipole moment of water, 1.84D, then the moment of the O—H bond is represented by the vector b and the following relationships hold:

$$OB = \tfrac{1}{2}OA = a$$

and

$$\frac{a}{b} = \cos 52.25° = \frac{\tfrac{1}{2}\mu_{H_2O}}{\mu_{H-O}}$$

$$\mu_{H-O} = \frac{\tfrac{1}{2}\mu_{H_2O}}{\cos 52.25°} = \frac{0.92}{0.61} = 1.51$$

The solution of this equation gives the vector dipole of the H—O bond as 1.51 Debye units.

The dipole moment of a molecule is a reflection of its polar or nonpolar character. In part, the polar character of a molecule determines its solvent properties (page 19). When we said that "like dissolves like," the chemical explanation of this dissolving ability depended mostly on finding polar or nonpolar character in the molecule.

The transition in solvent power from water to methyl alcohol to diethyl ether (dimethyl ether is a gas) is due in part to the decrease in polar character (Table 6.1) of the bonding, since the bond angles are comparable. Since the dipole moment only diminishes slightly in going from water (1.84D) to methanol (1.62D) to diethyl ether (1.22D) and does not vanish as it does in the symmetrical molecules CCl_4 and benzene, we may expect that other factors need to be considered in determining solubility. Nevertheless, the dipole moment will be some aid in predicting solubilities in various solvents. Vector resolution may be used to determine moments of other bonds in the following way. The bond angle in dimethyl ether has been determined by electron diffraction measurements to be $111 \pm 3°$ (Fig. 6.3) and the measured dipole moment is 1.29D (Table 6.1). From this a moment of 1.14D for

FIGURE 6.2 *Vector representation of the dipole moment of water. The bond angle in water is 104.5°; $\theta = 52.25°$. Vector OH represents the moment of the H—O bond. Vector OA represents the dipole moment of the molecule, HOH.*

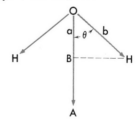

Table 6.1 DIPOLE MOMENTS OF MOLECULES OF VARIOUS LIQUIDS
(DEBYE UNITS)

H_2O	1.84	CH_3OCH_3	1.29 (vapor)
CH_3OH	1.62	$C_2H_5OC_2H_5$	1.22
C_2H_5OH	1.66		
$n\text{-}C_4H_9OH$	1.69	CCl_4	0
CH_3COOH	1.68	benzene, C_6H_6	0
$HCOOH$	1.77		

the CH_3—O bond may be calculated using the following trigonometric relationship:

$$2\mu_{CH_3-O} \times \cos 55.5° = 1.29D$$

$$\mu_{CH_3-O} = 1.14D$$

If these two numerical values, $\mu_{H-O} = 1.51D$ and $\mu_{CH_3-O} = 1.14D$ are assumed to be constant and transferable to the methyl alcohol molecule, then dipole moments may be calculated for reasonable bond angles in the methyl alcohol molecule. The vector relationship is:

For
$$\mu^2_{CH_3-OH} = \mu^2_{H-O} + \mu^2_{CH_3-O} + \mu_{H-O} \times \mu_{CH_3-O} \times \cos \theta$$

$$\theta = 110°, \quad \mu = 1.55D$$
$$\theta = 105°, \quad \mu = 1.61D$$
$$\theta = 102°, \quad \mu = 1.69D$$

The measured moment for methyl alcohol, 1.62D, allows a reasonable bond angle for the alcohol, near that of water, 104.5°.

The polar character of water and methyl alcohol arising from the strongly electronegative oxygen and the bond angle allows us to account for the associated nature of these two liquids in terms of hydrogen bonding (cf. pages 14–19). The polar character and hydrogen bonding accounts for the high boiling points of these two liquids in comparison with dimethyl ether (Table 2.3), which is polar but incapable of forming intermolecular hydrogen bridges. The possibility of hydrogen bonding in alcohols but not in ethers may give rise to sizable differences in solubilities in these two classes of solvents, despite the small difference in polar character.

Geometry of Molecules Containing OH Groups

When one H in HOH is replaced by a central atom M, the bond angle *MOH* is changed scarcely more than the uncertainty of measurement ($\pm 2°$) (Fig. 6.4). We will often not be interested in such a small difference. If M

FIGURE 6.3 *Bond angles in (a) water, (b) methyl alcohol, and (c) dimethyl ether.*

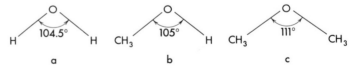

a b c

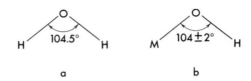

FIGURE 6.4 *Bond angles in (a)* HOH *and (b)* MOH.

a   b

holds several OH groups or OH and other groups, our interest will shift to the arrangement around the central atom M rather than to the bond angle at oxygen.

The bond angle at which an OH group is held with respect to some other atom attached to the central atom will depend on the number of groups (of all kinds) held by the central atom. The geometry may be described and accounted for by directed valence pictures in terms of the atomic orbital theory and hybridization, or more simply by the valence shell electron-pair repulsion theory.[1] The latter theory proposes that the geometry of a central atom is determined by the repulsions of bonding electron pairs and the still stronger repulsions of nonbonding electron pairs (lone pairs) in the valence shell. This is simply a consequence of considering that electrons repel each other and stay as far apart as they can. Even when forced to pair up by the strong attraction of positive nuclei, the electron *pairs* remain as far apart as possible.

Thus, two electron pairs (or two single electrons) should remain on opposite sides of a nucleus in a linear arrangement. By this theory three electron pairs (or three single electrons) should take a planar triangular arrangement about the nucleus. The most common arrangement (eight electrons in the valence shell) should find four electron pairs at the corners of a tetrahedron about the central atom. If we allow shared pairs to be represented by a straight line between two nuclei, and lone pairs to be represented by a shape similar to that in Fig. 6.5, then various examples (formulas) can be drawn (Fig. 6.6) where M represents a central atom (dark circle), A represents a group sharing a pair of electrons with M (light circle), and e represents a lone pair (Fig. 6.5).

How can we fit various series of compounds into the general formulas of Fig. 6.6? In the series MA_2, MA_3, MA_4, we may set as examples $BeBr_2$, BBr_3, CBr_4 for which we would suggest linear, triangular (trigonal plane), and tetrahedral shapes, respectively (Fig. 6.6). The corresponding hydroxy compounds are not all known but the series $Be(OH)_2$, $B(OH)_3$, and $Si(OH)_4$ would be expected to have the same shapes. In $B(OH)_3$, the expected $O—B—O$ bond angle is $120°$ and the measured bond angle is $120°$ within experimental error. The other two have not been measured.

What could we expect for other hydroxy compounds in which the central atom does not have the same groups A attached to M but which would fit variations such as $MABe$, MA_2B, $MABC$, etc? We can still be guided by the original assumption that electron pairs repel each other as far as possible, though the bond angles may now be distorted from lack of symmetry. The distortion away from the normal angles can be predicted in a

FIGURE 6.5 *Orbital shape of a lone pair of electrons about a central atom.*

[1] R. J. Gillespie, *J. Chem. Ed.*, **40**, 295 (1963).

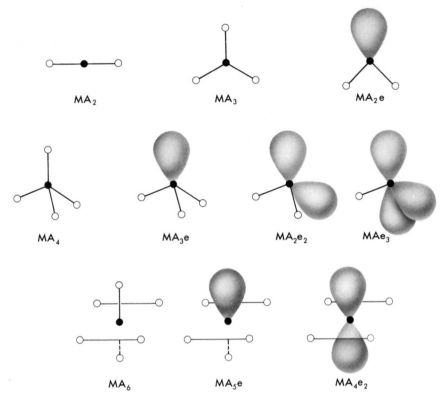

MA₂ MA₃ MA₂e

MA₄ MA₃e MA₂e₂ MAe₃

MA₆ MA₅e MA₄e₂

FIGURE 6.6 *Shapes of molecules with central atom M surrounded by groups A (represented by circles ◯) with shared pairs and lone pairs, e, with orbital shape from Fig. 6.5 [from J. Chem. Ed., **40**, 295 (1963)].*

qualitative way by using reasonable arguments concerning expected repulsions in the individual situations.

For the nitrous acid molecule (fitting the formula MABe), there are no measured data but the lone pair on nitrogen should repel bonded pairs more than bonded pairs repel each other. The argument for this view is that bonded pairs are shared by two positive nuclei and hence from a shielding effect have less possibility of repelling other shared pairs. We would expect the bond angle $O—N=O$ to be smaller than 120°. In nitrites (NO_2^-), the nearest analogy, the measured bond angle is 115°. If the noted angle in HONO (Fig. 6.7) is 115°, then the hypothetical bond angles at the lone pair, in agreement with the present argument, would be greater than 120°.

In the flat planar nitric acid molecule the added double bond character (resulting in shorter bond distances) should give increased repulsion between oxygens and widen the ONO bond angle at the expense of the two $ONOH$ bond angles. The measured bond angles can be reconciled with this argument: angle $ONO = 134°$ and (two) angles $ONOH = 113°$ (Fig. 6.7).

In acetic acid the flat planar molecule has a normal trigonal bond angle CCO, measured as 120.5°.

The series in Fig. 6.6 of general formulas MA_4, MA_3e, MA_2e_2, and MAe_3 is exemplified by the isoelectronic molecules CH_4, NH_3, H_2O, and HF, respectively (Fig. 6.8). We would expect the tetrahedral molecule CH_4 to be

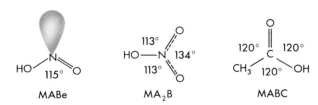

FIGURE 6.7   *Bond angles in one V-shaped and two planar molecules.*

completely symmetrical, and hence the bond angle HCH should be 109°28′, dictated solely by tetrahedral geometry. The tetrahedral nature of carbon is so well established that no one would bother to measure the angles in such an MA_4 molecule!

The argument that shared electron pairs (since the pair is attracted by two nuclei) repel each other less than they repel lone pairs would lead to an angle HNH in NH_3 of less than 109°28′. The measured angle is 107°20′.

Two lone pairs in the water molecule should repel each other more than they repel shared pairs, and so the angle HOH in water should be still smaller than the corresponding angle in ammonia. The measured angle in water is 104°28′.

The HF molecule is of necessity linear since the two nuclei determine a straight line and there is no measurement we can make to see if the argument given for NH_3 and H_2O holds in HF.

In a series of compounds of formula MA_3e (Fig. 6.6; the Group V halides), the deviations from tetrahedral angles are much more pronounced. Again the rule is followed that shared pairs repel each other less than lone pairs. The angles in the antimony series are smaller with the more electronegative halogen: SbF_3, 88°; $SbCl_3$, 96°; $SbBr_3$, 97°; $AsBr_3$, 100°; AsI_3, 101°; PF_3, 104°; PCl_3, 100°; PBr_3, 101°; PI_3, 102°. Only one compound of the nitrogen series (NF_3) has been subjected to bond angle measurements (102.5°).

In the series of compounds $(HO)_4Si$, $(HO)_3PO$, $(HO)_2SO_2$, and $HOClO_3$, for which the general formulas MA_4, MA_3B, MA_2B_2, and MAB_3 could be written, we would expect each of the four molecules to be tetrahedral. However, regular tetrahedra would not be expected in the last three, since the bond distance from the central atom to O would not be the same as the distance to OH. Another way to say this is that bond distance between any two atoms decreases with increase in double bond character (exaggerated in

FIGURE 6.8   *Geometry of four isoelectronic molecules.*

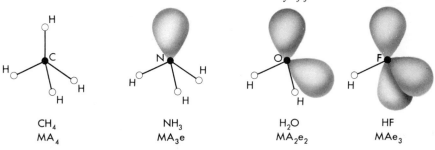

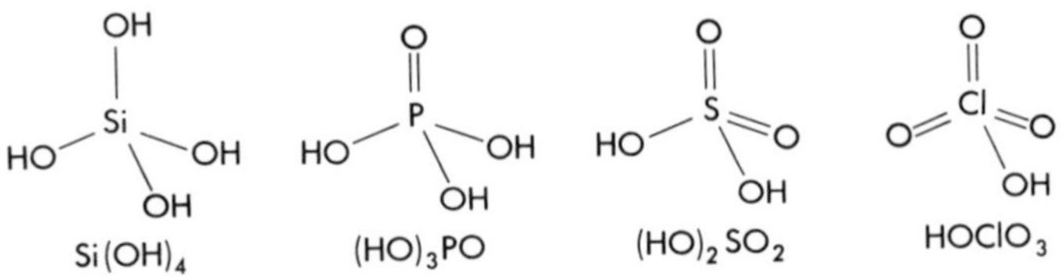

Si(OH)$_4$ (HO)$_3$PO   (HO)$_2$SO$_2$ HOClO$_3$

FIGURE 6.9   *Tetrahedral structures of* Si(OH)$_4$, (HO)$_3$PO, (HO)$_2$SO$_2$, *and* HOClO$_3$, *showing the unsymmetrical character of the last three.*

Fig. 6.9). Measurements of bond lengths in related compounds suggest that this argument is valid although bond angles have not been measured in these four acids.

In compounds with six groups around the central atom, mutual repulsions of shared pairs might be expected to give a symmetrical octahedral topology. The MA_6 formula of Fig. 6.6 is shown in better perspective by connecting the A's (OH's) as in Fig. 6.10. Octahedral geometry dictates 90° angles for all $OTeO$ bonds in Te(OH)$_6$. Another known hydroxy compound and two anions that fit this general formula are (HO)$_5$IO, Sb(OH)$_6^-$, and Sn(OH)$_6^=$. Direct measurements on bond angles have not been made in compounds of this type, but infrared and Raman spectra of some corresponding hexafluorides require octahedral symmetry for easy interpretation.

The Orbital Description of Bonding in Compounds with OH Groups

An alternative to the valence shell electron-pair repulsion theory of accounting for the geometry of molecules is an orbital description of bonding. As examples we will examine bonding in covalent compounds of Be, B, and C. In this series the ground state energy levels are described by the following symbols:

Be $1s^2$ $2s^2$

B $1s^2$ $2s^2$ $2p^1$

C $1s^2$ $2s^2$ $2p_x^1$ $2p_y^1$

When the outer orbitals of these three elements (and others) are used to account for the bonding in molecules, the combination with orbitals of the other atoms involved is said to give "hybridized molecular orbitals." The additive combination of orbitals of a given atom having nearly equal energies gives rise to the same number of hybridized orbitals. The mental gymnastics that chemists go through to account for the bonding in the final molecular state of these atoms are not necessarily a process that reflects occurrences in atoms and molecules. These gymnastics are a consequence of our inability to obtain exact solutions of the Schrödinger wave equation, and arise from the approximations employed. The orbital description is a mental model that chemists use to describe the end

FIGURE 6.10   *Octahedral structure of* Te(OH)$_6$.

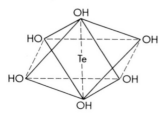

90

Table 6.2 ELECTRONIC DESCRIPTION OF HYBRIDIZED ORBITALS

	Be	B	C
ground state	$1s^2 2s^2$	$1s^2 2s^2 2p^1$	$1s^2 2s^2 2p_x{}^1 2p_y{}^1$
excited state	$1s^2 2s^1 2p^1$	$1s^2 2s^1 2p_x{}^1 2p_y{}^1$	$1s^2 2s^1 2p_x{}^1 2p_y{}^1 2p_z{}^1$
hybridized state	$2s^1 2p^1$	$2s^1 2p_x{}^1 2p_y{}^1$	$2s^1 2p_x{}^1 2p_y{}^1 2p_z{}^1$
hybridized orbitals	two sp	three sp^2	four sp^3
molecular orbital orientation			
bond angles	180°	120°	109°28'
geometry	linear	triangular	tetrahedral

result. In Table 6.2, the electronic configurations and resulting molecular geometry are described for Be, B, and C.

From the description in Table 6.2, we would expect that beryllium hydroxide [Be(OH)$_2$] would have linear O—Be—O geometry in two sp hybrid O—Be bonds. In B(OH)$_3$ we would expect sp^2 hybridization, resulting in bond angles of 120° for the three *OBO* bonds (compare the Nyholm and Gillespie theory, page 87). We would describe the bonding in Si(OH)$_4$ as four sp^3 hybrid Si—O bonds, which would result in tetrahedral geometry.

Since atomic p orbitals and the orbital axes are pictured in planes mutually perpendicular (Fig. 6.11) to each other, bond formation in molecular orbitals involving these p orbitals should give bond angles of 90° in maximum overlap either with other p orbitals or with s orbitals. In the two series of hydrides from Groups V and VI (Table 6.3), this appears to be the case for the lower elements in the groups (As, Sb, Se, Te in Group V, for example), but there is remarkable deviation from 90° in the bond angles of the hydrides of the first members, ammonia (from N, the first element in Group V) and water.

FIGURE 6.11 *Models of atomic p orbitals in x, y, and z planes and assembled in one three-dimensional perspective.*

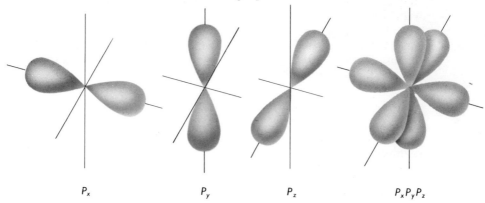

P_x P_y P_z $P_x P_y P_z$

Table 6.3 BOND ANGLES IN GROUPS V AND VI HYDRIDES

NH_3	107°20′	H_2O	104°28′
PH_3	93°20′	H_2S	92°10′
AsH_3	91°50′	H_2Se	91°
SbH_3	91°20′	H_2Te	89°30′

The deviation from 90° in bond angles of NH_3 is accounted for in the orbital theory by interposing the notion that some hybridization of the $2s$ orbital (of nitrogen) and the three $2p$ orbitals

$$N \qquad 1s^2 2s^2 2p_x^1 2p_y^1 2p_z^1$$

gives the three bonds in ammonia some sp^3 hybrid character. Such added s character to the bonding can be interpreted as a tendency in the direction of increased bond angle (90° → 109°28′)—that is, toward the normal sp^3 (tetrahedral) bond angle. The theory limps a little, since there does not appear on the face of it to be any substantial reason why the lower members of the Group V elements (P, As, and Sb) should form more nearly pure p bonds with angles very close to 90° (Table 6.3).

The deviation from 90° for the bond angles in water is accounted for in similar language. The $2s$ orbital of oxygen may be hybridized with the three $2p$ orbitals to give some sp^3 character to the bonding in water. But again we have difficulty finding a reason for the small deviations from 90° in bond angles of the other Group VI hydrides (Table 6.3).

In octahedral molecules the bonding in orbital terms will generally be d^2sp^3 hybrids. In tellurium for the compound $Te(OH)_6$, the d^2sp^3 hybridization may be represented as shown in Table 6.4.

The ground state of tellurium has six electrons in the fifth level (principal quantum number, 5). If these are (mentally) stripped from the atom, the Te^{6+} ion would now have a vacant fifth quantum level. Six OH ions bring six pairs (12 electrons) to the bonding in $Te(OH)_6$. The lowest electronic energy levels (orbitals) to be filled in the Te^{6+} skeleton are now six d^2sp^3 hybridized orbitals, $5s$ (two electrons), $5p$ ($6e$), and $5d$ ($4e$) rather than six unhybridized orbitals from $5s$, $5p$, and $6s$ (or $4f$) levels.

The remaining molecules, whose geometry was discussed in terms of valence shell electron-pair repulsions (page 87ff.), involve multiple bonds. In orbital terms, all single bonds, hybridized or not, are called sigma (σ) bonds. If two half-filled p orbitals remain on adjacent atoms in a molecule joined by sigma bonds, the possibility of sidewise overlap of p orbitals in π bonds obtains. Certain d orbitals may also overlap in π bonds. In such cases one may speak of d_π- or p_π-overlap.

Table 6.4 HYBRIDIZATION IN TELLURIUM

ground state	$_{52}Te$	$1s^2 2s^2 2p^6 3s^2 3p^6 3d^{10} 4s^2 4p^6 4d^{10}$	$5s^2$	$5p_x^2 5p_y^1 5p_z^1$	
ion (hypothetical)	Te^{6+}	$1s^2 2s^2 2p^6 3s^2 3p^6 3d^{10} 4s^2 4p^6 4d^{10}$			
molecule	$Te(OH)_6$	$1s^2 2s^2 2p^6 3s^2 3p^6 3d^{10} 4s^2 4p^6 4d^{10}$	$5s$	$5p$	$5d$

92

The bonding on the central atom in acetic acid first must involve three sigma bonds since the central carbon is attached to three other atoms. On this carbon, then, three sp^2 orbitals form the three sigma bonds, described by the symbols sp^2-p (underlined in the electronic structures shown for C and O). One half-filled p orbital remains on the

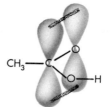

FIGURE 6.12 *The π bond in acetic acid, CH_3COOH.*

carbon and one on the oxygen both designated as $2p_z^1$ (below). The stage is set for sidewise overlap of these two p orbitals to form an additional bond—a π bond on the adjacent carbon and oxygen atoms (Fig. 6.12).

$$C \qquad 1s^2 \quad \underline{2s^12p_x^12p_y^1} \quad 2p_z^1$$
$$O \qquad 1s^2 \quad 2s^22p_x^2\underline{2p_y^1} \quad 2p_z^1$$

In nitric acid, the p_π overlap is smeared out over three atoms (nitrogen and two oxygen atoms) instead of two. In general, the more volume an electron can occupy, the lower will be the total energy of the system in which it is contained (Fig. 6.13).

In the molecules in Fig. 6.9, the bonding in silicic acid could be described simply as sp^3 hybridization. However, the central bonding in the tetrahedral molecules $(HO)_3PO$, $(HO)_2SO_2$, and $HOClO_3$ (Fig. 6.9) is not fairly described as simply sp^3 hybridization. The P—O, S—O, and Cl—O bonds are somewhat shorter than the P—OH, S—OH, or Cl—OH single bonds, respectively. This can be accounted for if the sp^3 hybrid (sigma) bonding is strengthened by additional pi character, resulting from d_π-p_π overlap of a d orbital of the central atoms P, S, and Cl, respectively, with a p orbital from oxygen.

Asymmetry in sp^3 Bonding

The third dimension inherently gives to sp^3 bonding one peculiarity that does not obtain in flat, planar structures [like $HONO_2$, $(HO)_2CO$, $B(OH)_3$, etc.], in linear molecules [like $Be(OH)_2$, $Hg(OH)_2$, etc.], nor in V-shaped molecules (like HOH). When four different groups are attached to a tetrahedral central atom, M*abcd*, there are two ways of arranging the groups that are distinguishable in the physical model.

The two models R and S in Fig. 6.14 are not superimposable and hence they may be distinguished. They are like right- and left-handed gloves which have a certain symmetry but not perfect symmetry (else they would be interchangeable). We may also say that R is a mirror image of S, since they would be related in that way if an imaginary mirror were placed perpendicular to the paper at the dotted line in Fig. 6.14.

Is this just a fact of geometry, or does it have a connection with chemistry? Indeed,

FIGURE 6.13 *The p_π overlap in nitric acid, $HONO_2$.*

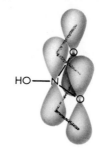

HO—N

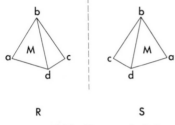

R   S

FIGURE 6.14 *Two tetrahedral structures, R and S, for the general formula* M*abcd*.

historically, it was the chemistry that led to the geometry, rather than the reverse. The knowledge that two compounds of the general formula M*abcd* (with carbon as the central atom M) were recognized by chemists led Le Bel and van't Hoff in 1874 to suggest independently that the carbon atom was tetrahedral as well as tetravalent. The tetravalence had been recognized in 1858 by Kekulé. The consequences of the existence of two forms (R and S) of a compound could most easily be accounted for if the four groups *a*, *b*, *c*, and *d* were attached at the corners of a tetrahedron with the carbon atom at the center. No evidence has been found since 1874 which makes this theory untenable. Furthermore, no case has been found in which more than two compounds of formula C*abcd* have been discovered. It was the theory of Le Bel and van't Hoff that introduced to chemists the idea that the third dimension is important.

Exercise 6.1. Suppose that the molecule C*abcd* was a square planar structure with C at the center. How many structures can be drawn having the formula C*abcd*?

Exercise 6.2. Suppose that a molecule C*abcd* was rectangular with C at the center. How many structures can be drawn having the formula C*abcd*?

How much difference is there between the properties of the two compounds of the same formula C*abcd*? Suppose that we take as a specific example the alcohol having the formula

$$\overset{4}{C}H_3-\overset{3}{C}H_2-\overset{2}{*}CH-\overset{1}{C}H_2-OH$$
$$|$$
$$CH_3$$

If the carbon bearing the asterisk (C2 according to the Geneva system) be considered the carbon at the center of the tetrahedron, the three-dimensional perspective formulas R and S (Fig. 6.15) can be drawn in which *a* in the formula C*abcd* is CH_3, *b* is C_2H_5, *c* is CH_2OH, and *d* is H.

Exercise 6.3. What is the Geneva name of the alcohol?

For purposes of enabling chemists to represent three-dimensional structures such as R and S in two dimensions, it is convenient to use projection formulas (Fig. 6.16). Projection formulas, however, require certain conventions to guard against errors in interpretation.

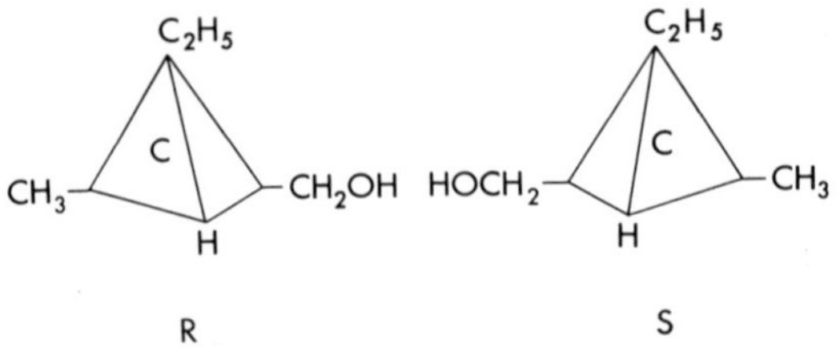

FIGURE 6.15 *Two structures, R and S, of formula*

$$CH_3-CH_2-\overset{*}{C}H-CH_2OH$$
$$|$$
$$CH_3$$

(three-dimensional perspective).

94

FIGURE 6.16 *Two structures, R and S, of formula*

$$CH_3CH_2\overset{*}{\underset{|}{C}}H\!\!-\!\!CH_2OH$$
$$\overset{|}{CH_3}$$

(*two-dimensional projection*).

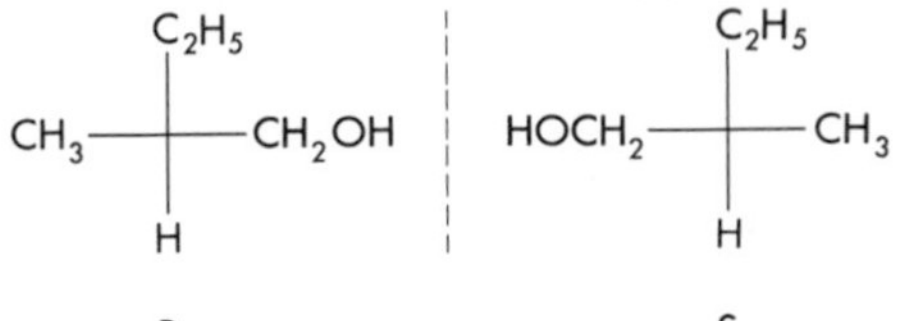

$$CH_3\!\!-\!\!\overset{\overset{\displaystyle C_2H_5}{|}}{\underset{\underset{\displaystyle H}{|}}{C}}\!\!-\!\!CH_2OH$$

R

$$HOCH_2\!\!-\!\!\overset{\overset{\displaystyle C_2H_5}{|}}{\underset{\underset{\displaystyle H}{|}}{C}}\!\!-\!\!CH_3$$

S

1. If in Fig. 6.15 the groups CH_3, C_2H_5, and CH_2OH in the three-dimensional model are in the plane of the paper, and the central carbon and H are in front of the paper, then the corresponding projections in two dimensions are those of Fig. 6.16.

2. If rotations *in the plane of the paper* produce superposition of two projection formulas, the formulas are identical. If not, the formulas represent stereoisomers. (By this convention, which of the two stereoisomers, R or S, in Fig. 6.16, is represented in Fig. 6.17?)

Mistakes in interpretation will be made if the formulas are taken out of the plane of the paper to accomplish superposition. For example, the two forms R and S (Fig. 6.16), which we have said are different, can be superimposed by folding the figure on the dotted line. That manipulation is forbidden by this convention.

Exercise 6.4. Draw the three-dimensional perspective formulas for the following projection formulas.

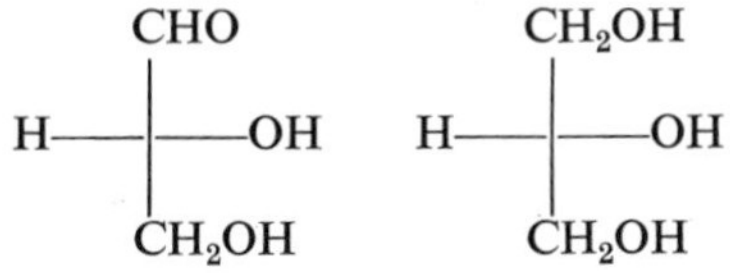

$$\begin{array}{c} CHO \\ | \\ H\!-\!\!-\!\!-\!\!-OH \\ | \\ CH_2OH \end{array}$$
(a)

$$\begin{array}{c} CH_2OH \\ | \\ H\!-\!\!-\!\!-\!\!-OH \\ | \\ CH_2OH \end{array}$$
(b)

Exercise 6.5. Would the mirror image of (a) in Exercise 6.4 be superimposable on (a)? (b) on (b)?

The startling thing about the two (R and S) forms of this alcohol is that all the properties but one are exactly the same. Besides the first three properties given in Table 6.5, all the chemical reactions are also exactly the same for the R and S forms of the alcohol. The fourth property[2] (Table 6.5) is different for the R and S forms of 2-methyl-1-butanol.

The alcohol that we have mentioned (2-methyl-1-butanol) is one of the constituents of "fusel oil," the higher-boiling residue left in the fermentation of glucose by yeast after the main product (ethyl alcohol, C_2H_5OH) is distilled

FIGURE 6.17 *R or S? (See Fig. 6.16.)*

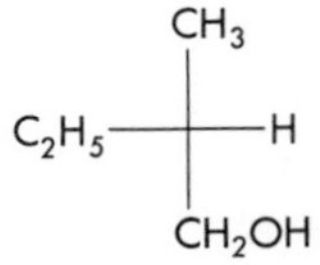

$$C_2H_5\!\!-\!\!\overset{\overset{\displaystyle CH_3}{|}}{\underset{\underset{\displaystyle CH_2OH}{|}}{C}}\!\!-\!\!H$$

---

[2] In the case of some biologically active compounds it is not quite true that the R and S forms always act exactly alike. For example, the enzymes from certain bacteria may metabolize the R form (or the S form) of a compound and not touch the other. This must mean that the bacteria can recognize the configurational difference of an R and an S form in the same sense that you can recognize a left-hand glove without having a right-hand glove present, and without even looking at your left hand. (The chemist has not been able to recognize the difference between an R and an S form in the laboratory without special optically active agents.)

Table 6.5 PROPERTIES OF THREE KINDS OF 2-METHYL-1-BUTANOL

	(R) 2-methyl-1-butanol	(S) 2-methyl-1-butanol	(RS) 2-methyl-1-butanol
bp, °C	128	128	129.4
d_4^{25}	0.8158	0.8158	0.8152
n_D^{20}	1.4102	1.4102	1.4092
α_D^{20}	$+5.90°$	$-5.90°$	$0.°$

from the fermented mixture. In the fermentation process, the S form only ($\alpha_D^{20} = -5.90°$) of 2-methyl-1-butanol appears in the "fusel oil." The compound is said to be "optically active" since the plane of polarized light passing through the compound is rotated counterclockwise (*levo*) as one looks toward the source of light. That is, the rotation (α) of plane polarized light (the sodium D line) at $20°$ is $-5.90°$ when the path length is 10 cm.

Every compound that has been found to be optically active has an asymmetric structure. The compounds are either asymmetric in the way that we have shown for compounds of formula $Cabcd$ (that is, with four different groups attached to a central atom), or the molecule as a whole is asymmetric.

The phenomenon of optical activity is observed in numerous compounds that occur in nature. The sugars that occur in nature (glucose, fructose, sucrose, lactose, maltose, and others) are all optically active alcohols in which several carbon atoms are asymmetric. Of the 20 amino acids that are building-blocks for proteins, all but one are optically active.

Polyalcohols

The instability of two OH groups on the same carbon in all but a few exceptional compounds was indicated earlier (page 60). Intramolecular loss of water generally resulted (Eqs. 4.13–4.15) in such compounds where multiple OH groups occurred on the same carbon. However, OH groups on adjacent or more remote carbon atoms in a chain are not at all incompatible; in general, each one does contribute to the total properties of the compound.

In Fig. 6.18, three polyalcohols of commercial importance—ethyleneglycol, glycerol, and sorbitol—are shown in projection formulas (carbon atoms at line intersections are understood).

Ethyleneglycol, produced at the rate of a billion pounds per year, is used principally as a "permanent" antifreeze, and as a humectant for tobacco. Glycerol, the production of which runs to about 250 million pounds per year, is used to manufacture explosives (dynamite), as a humectant, in the manufacture of alkyd resins (refrigerator fronts and the like), as a softening agent for cellophane, and in making emulsifying agents. Sorbitol, produced to the extent of 150 million pounds per year (an estimate, since figures are not available) by the catalytic hydrogenation of glucose (grape sugar), is the starting point for the synthesis of ascorbic acid (Vitamin C).

One effect of the multiple OH groups in all three compounds is to increase the attraction for water in forming intermolecular hydrogen bonds (p. 15ff.). The use of these compounds as humectants depends on this ability to attract moisture from the air. Tobacco leaves (for example) do not dry out in the presence of such substances. Polyalcohols like sorbitol (mp $97°$), as a consequence of this attraction for water, are difficult to crystallize, and tend to form syrups and supersaturated solutions.

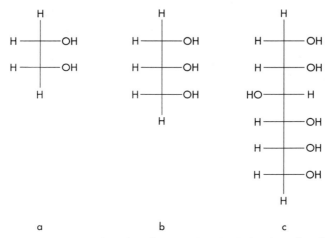

FIGURE 6.18 *Projection formulas of (a) ethyleneglycol, (b) glycerol, and (c) sorbitol.*

The high viscosity of ethyleneglycol and glycerol depends on the possibility of forming multiple and interlocking hydrogen bonds among the many OH groups within and between molecules. Since the total van der Waals force on a single molecule is so high (because of the numerous attractions of other molecules), these liquids are viscous, and have high boiling points in comparison with compounds of like molecular mass (Table 6.6).

The ubiquitous OH group (one for each carbon) makes these compounds polar in character, and they are miscible with water. The same circumstance decreases the solubility in hydrocarbons and ether ("like dissolves like"; page 19). Sorbitol is only sparingly soluble in ethyl alcohol (less polar than water).

Although the character of these polyalcohols depends on the accumulation of OH groups, the chemical reactions of one OH group are not generally different because of the presence of the other OH's. In most cases each OH acts independently in the reaction. This means that the chemistry of the polyalcohols is not different in kind from that of the alcohols themselves. For example, the reaction we wrote for an alcohol with HBr will simply take two moles of reagent in the reaction with ethyleneglycol.

$$\begin{matrix} CH_2\text{—}OH \\ | \\ CH_2\text{—}OH \end{matrix} + 2\ HBr \xrightarrow{H_2SO_4} \begin{matrix} CH_2\text{—}Br \\ | \\ CH_2\text{—}Br \end{matrix} + 2\ H_2O \qquad \text{(Eq. 6.1)}$$

It is important to note, however, that though the chemical reaction may be the same, the end result may have quite different consequences. For example, although an alcohol and an acid can be made to react to form an ester (Eq. 2.40), if a polyalcohol is used with a dicarboxylic acid, a completely different end result may ensue. The reaction of terephthalic acid with methanol gives a well-behaved crystalline product (Eq. 6.2).

Table 6.6 BOILING POINTS (°C) OF HYDROXY COMPOUNDS

CH₃OH	65°	ethyleneglycol	197°
HOH	100°	glycerol	290° (decomposes)

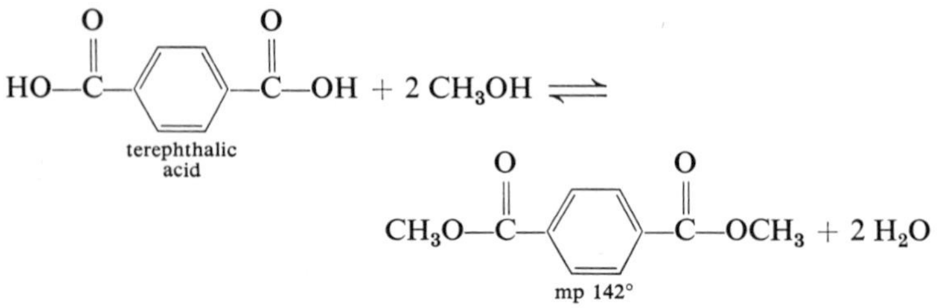

$$HO-\overset{\overset{O}{\|}}{C}-\langle\bigcirc\rangle-\overset{\overset{O}{\|}}{C}-OH + 2\,CH_3OH \rightleftharpoons$$

terephthalic acid

$$CH_3O-\overset{\overset{O}{\|}}{C}-\langle\bigcirc\rangle-\overset{\overset{O}{\|}}{C}-OCH_3 + 2\,H_2O \quad \text{(Eq. 6.2)}$$

mp 142°

With ethyleneglycol (Eq. 6.3) and the same acid, a high-molecular-mass polymer is formed which may be drawn out into threads (Dacron.)

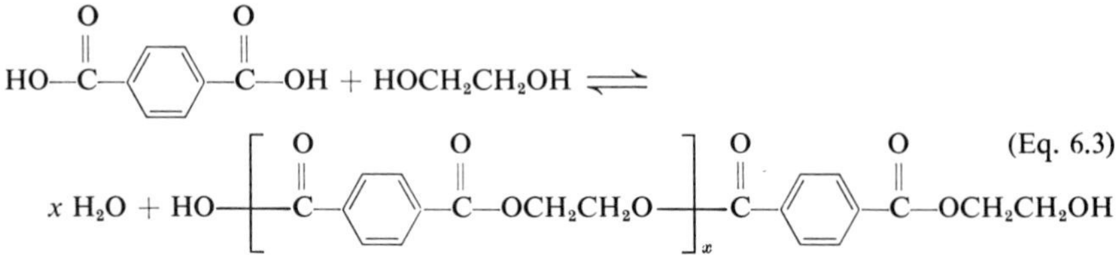

$$HO-\overset{\overset{O}{\|}}{C}-\langle\bigcirc\rangle-\overset{\overset{O}{\|}}{C}-OH + HOCH_2CH_2OH \rightleftharpoons$$

$$x\,H_2O + HO-\left[\overset{\overset{O}{\|}}{C}-\langle\bigcirc\rangle-\overset{\overset{O}{\|}}{C}-OCH_2CH_2O\right]_x-\overset{\overset{O}{\|}}{C}-\langle\bigcirc\rangle-\overset{\overset{O}{\|}}{C}-OCH_2CH_2OH \quad \text{(Eq. 6.3)}$$

Dacron, a polymer

Reaction of glycerol with the same acid gives a polymer with free OH groups along the chain that may "cross-link" in ester linkages by the same reaction to give "cross-linked" polymers (Exp. 6.4). Alkyd resins are of this type in which a three-dimensional network polymer can eventually be formed. (Compare the silicate network polymers, Fig. 4.7.)

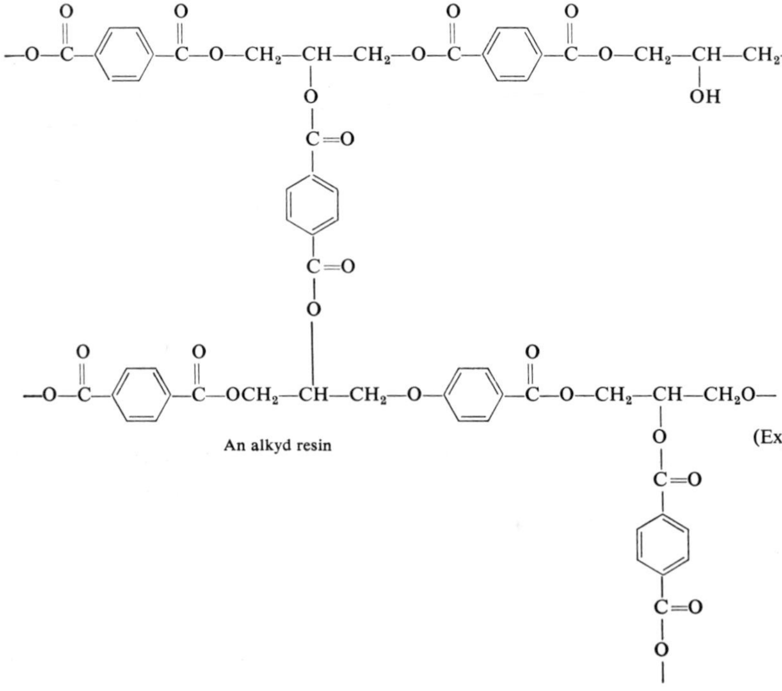

An alkyd resin

(Exp. 6.4)

Sugars

Closely related to the polyalcohols is a group of compounds called *carbohydrates*, of which one significant type is the sugars. Indeed, sugars *are* polyalcohols, although they contain one additional functional group, a carbonyl function (page 60). The simplest sugar contains three carbons, since to qualify as a *poly* alcohol it must contain at least two OH groups and the carbonyl function. The function

$$-\overset{|}{\underset{H}{C}}=O$$

is called an aldehyde group. The compound containing three carbons (Fig. 6.19) is called glyceraldehyde (related to glycerol).

The sugars are classified as monosaccharides (three to six carbons), disaccharides, and polysaccharides, the latter of which can be hydrolyzed to monosaccharides. The most common sugar of all, table sugar (sucrose), of molecular formula $C_{12}H_{22}O_{11}$, can be hydrolyzed to two monosaccharides, glucose and fructose, which are isomers.

$$\underset{\text{sucrose}}{C_{12}H_{22}O_{11}} + H_2O \xrightarrow{H^+} \underset{\text{glucose}}{C_6H_{12}O_6} + \underset{\text{fructose}}{C_6H_{12}O_6} \qquad \text{(Eq. 6.5)}$$

The Third Dimension in the Sugars

In glyceraldehyde, Fig. 6.19, let us look closely at the space relationships on each of the three carbons. Carbon 1 carries three groups and has flat planar geometry, or in orbital terms—sp^2 (p. 90ff.). Carbons 2 and 3 have sp^3 bonding, and hence asymmetry is possible. Carbon 2 is indeed asymmetric, since four different groups (H, CHO, OH, and CH_2OH; Fig. 6.19b) are joined to the central atom. Carbon 3 is not asymmetric (Fig. 6.19c), since two of the four groups (H, H, OH, and CHOH—CHO) are identical.

The consequence of asymmetry at carbon 2 in glyceraldehyde is that there are two ways to arrange the four groups about this carbon.

Exercise 6.6. Sketch perspective pictures of the two forms (mirror images) of glyceraldehyde, using Fig. 6.19b as one model.

FIGURE 6.19 (a) Glyceraldehyde, showing sp^3 bonding at (b) C2 and (c) C3.

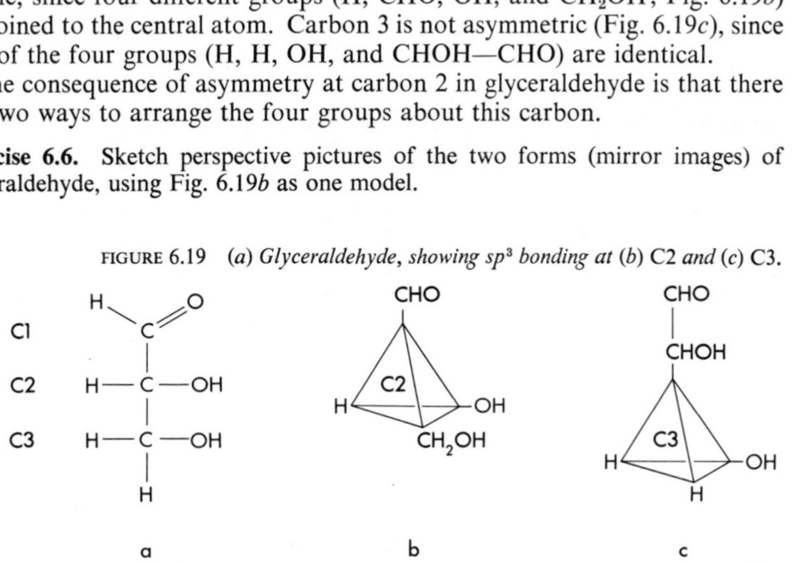

a   b   c

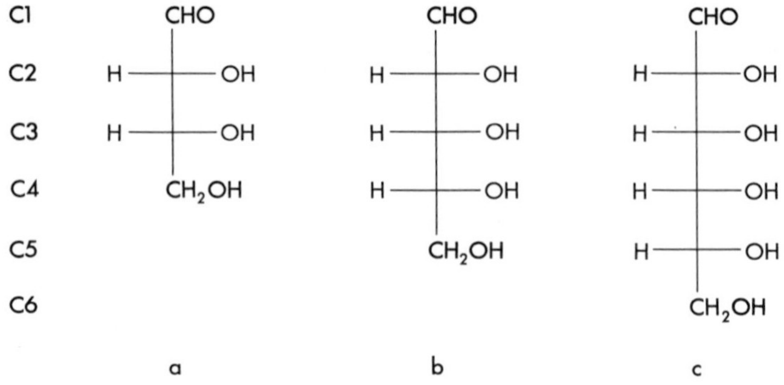

C1	CHO	CHO	CHO
C2	H——OH	H——OH	H——OH
C3	H——OH	H——OH	H——OH
C4	CH₂OH	H——OH	H——OH
C5		CH₂OH	H——OH
C6			CH₂OH
	a	b	c

FIGURE 6.20 *Projection formulas of sugars of (a) four carbons, (b) five carbons, and (c) six carbons.*

In the four-carbon sugar (Fig. 6.20a) there are two asymmetric carbons (C2 and C3), since each of these carbons carries four different groups (C1 is an sp^2 carbon, of course). On C2, the four groups are H, CHO, OH, and CHOH—CH₂OH. On C3, the four groups are H, CHOH—CHO, OH, and CH₂OH. With two asymmetric carbons the total number of isomers is $2^2 = 4$. The projection formulas of these four isomers are shown in Fig. 6.21 as two pairs of mirror images, (a and b) and (c and d). The perspective formulas for joined tetrahedra are not easy to show on paper and it is not at all convincing in two dimensions that four isomers of Fig. 6.20a exist. The reader himself must make the four (ball and stick) models to be sure that no two of them can be superimposed. In Fig. 6.21, models (a) and (c) are not mirror images but are not superimposable, and models (b) and (d) also are not mirror images but are not superimposable.

When three asymmetric carbons (all different) are present in a molecule, eight (2^3) isomers are possible, and with four asymmetric carbons, 16 (2^4) isomers are possible. The eight isomers may be described as four pairs of mirror images, and the 16 isomers as eight pairs of mirror images. The general formula, then, for the number of isomers in a compound with n asymmetric carbons is 2^n, and they are described as 2^{n-1} mirror images.

In the six-carbon sugars (Fig. 6.20c) there are 16 possible compounds with this same structural formula. When we contemplate that the properties must be very similar since the same groups are present in all of them, it is more understandable that chemists took nearly 50 years (about 1870–1920) to

FIGURE 6.21 *Projection formulas for four isomeric four-carbon sugars shown as two pairs of mirror images: (a) and (b); and (c) and (d).*

CHO	CHO	CHO	CHO
H——OH	HO——H	H——OH	HO——H
H——OH	HO——H	HO——H	H——OH
CH₂OH	CH₂OH	CH₂OH	CH₂OH
a	b	c	d

100

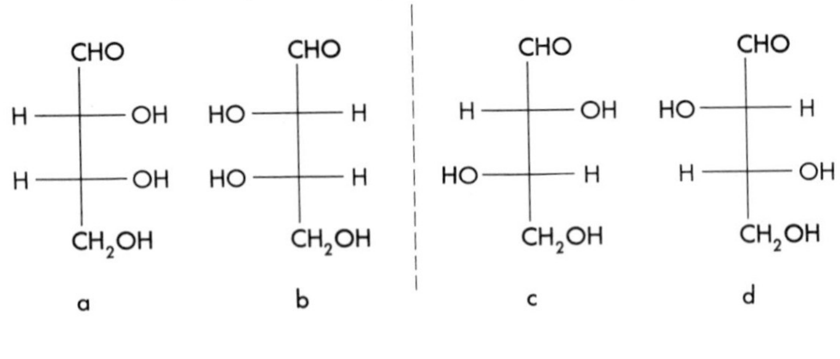

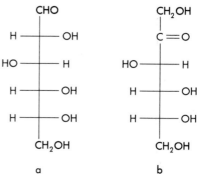

FIGURE 6.22 (a) *Glucose and* (b) *fructose are products of the hydrolysis of sucrose.*

identify completely the 16 sugars and to delineate their properties. The problem of identification of all the six-carbon sugars was further complicated by the fact that the carbonyl function does not necessarily have to reside in carbon 1.

This complication does, in fact, occur. The two sugars, glucose and fructose (Fig. 6.22), that result from the hydrolysis of sucrose (Eq. 6.5) are not both aldehyde sugars. In fructose the carbonyl function is on carbon 2. Fructose is therefore a ketone sugar (compare acetone, Eq. 4.15) rather than an aldehyde sugar. The structures of these two sugars are identical on C3, C4, and C5.

A more complete picture of sugar chemistry must await your subsequent venture into organic chemistry.

Exercise 6.7. Write structural formulas for each of the following compounds and determine the number of asymmetric carbon atoms (if any) in each of the following examples:

a. $(CH_3)_2CH—CHOH—CH_3$
b. $(CH_3)_2COH—CHOH—CH_3$
c. $(CH_3)COH—CHOH—CHO$
d. $CH_3—CHOH—CHOH—CHO$
e. $CH_3—CHOH—COOH$
f. $CH_2OH—CHOH—CHOH—COOH$

Exercise 6.8. What is the total number of space isomers in each of the compounds of Exercise 6.7?

Exercise 6.9. How many of the isomeric five-carbon alcohols (Exercise 1.3) contain asymmetric carbons?

Exercise 6.10. Write the structure of one alcohol of formula $C_6H_{14}O$ that should exhibit optical activity.

Index